Adventures on the Quest

Richard and Mary-Alice Jafolla

A COMPANION TO

The Quest GUIDEBOOK

unity® HOUSE

Unity Village, Missouri

Seventh printing 2005

Published by the Unity Movement Advisory Council, a joint committee of the Association of Unity Churches and Unity.

To place an order, call the Customer Service Department at 1-800-669-0282 or visit us online at *www.unityonline.org.*
Cover photo © J. A. Kraulis/Masterfile
Cover photo of Dhaulagiri and Tukuche Peaks, Nepal
Authors' photo by Kim Crenshaw
Cover designed by Chad Pio
Text designed by Linda Gates

Library of Congress Catalog Card Number: 92-063344
ISBN 0-87159-274-6 (Activity Book)
ISBN 0-87159-277-0 (Set)
Canada BN 13252 9033 RT

TABLE OF CONTENTS

INTRODUCTION

This Activity Book is your *Quest* companion. It will serve as a bridge to take you from the teachings of the Guidebook to their adventures in everyday life.

The value of any adventure lies in its ability to lift us to higher ground—to serve as a stepping-stone to a better life. Think of this Activity Book, then, as a hand-holding companion to lead you ahead on your journey of rediscovery. Follow along with us, step-by-step, as you bring each new adventure to life.

FOLLOW THE MAP

There is really only one way to journey on your quest: systematically. Imagine how little progress you'd make if you set out on an expedition and then didn't follow your maps. With no definite plan or purpose, you would soon be lost, overwhelmed by your surroundings. The same applies to *The Quest*. To attempt it in a directionless, undisciplined manner would only lead to confusion and frustration.

The Quest is a progressive, evolutionary process. It is going to move you into unknown territory. Right now you are at the start of your expedition. Are you willing to go the distance? You have to make that commitment to yourself if you intend to attain the treasure of transformation. *The Quest* requires that you proceed with purpose and self-discipline, one day at a time, one step at a time, until you've completed the process.

BASE CAMP

You may be tempted to skip over an activity that seems too basic, too elementary, for your present level of spiritual maturity, but it's good to touch base with the fundamentals. Somehow we never really outgrow them. A circling back can only strengthen you and give you impetus to reach for further heights.

Vince Lombardi, the Hall of Fame football coach, believed strongly in basics. He felt it was the key to the great success of his teams. Legend has it that Lombardi was so dedicated to the basic fundamentals of the game that, in order to make the point with his players, he began each new football camp the same way. Addressing his players, most of whom had already been playing the game for more than a decade, he would hold a football above his head and say, "Gentlemen, this is a football."

A friend told us a story about a chemistry class he took. The class was made up mostly of chemistry majors, with a handful of physics majors like himself who were required to take the course. On the first day of class, the professor announced: "The physics majors will do better than you chemistry majors, and here's why. We'll be starting with basic chemistry but there will be a few new twists. Of course, the physics majors will study this because it's all new to them. But you chemistry majors will not study because you think you know the basics, and when the course heads into new territory, you chemistry people will not be properly prepared." As it turned out, his predictions were right on target.

2

We like to think of the basic level of *The Quest* as a kind of base camp for our expedition. Participating in these early maneuvers will serve to give you a solid footing for progressing deeper into the journey. It will give your quest a sense of wholeness and completeness. Even a climb up the highest mountain begins in the foothills.

The bottom line is that the basics are important. Professionals practice basics long into their careers. Musicians play scales, dancers practice positions, athletes hone techniques, all in an attempt to perfect basic fundamentals. It is to your advantage to follow this Activity Book as it is laid out, conscientiously completing each activity before going on to the next.

FOR THE ADVENTURER

Rising up behind the shore of the French Riviera are mountains which can be traveled by way of three roads called "corniches." Closest to sea level is *La Corniche Inferieure*, providing safety and attractive local scenery. Then comes *La Moyenne Corniche* for those who want a medium altitude with wonderful views of the coast below. Above that is *La Grande Corniche* for travelers who want the most spectacular views. This road is very high and full of unexpected twists and turns. It is for people who want to make the extra effort required to traverse the peaks. Travel is slower and the experience quite intense, but the views are absolutely sensational. As you would expect, there is very little traffic up there.

La Grande Corniche is not used by people who are interested in getting from one place to another in the safest, most direct way. It is off the main trail, available when one simply feels the need of a more intense experience. For most travel, however, the other roads are much more practical and preferable.

The Quest, like the mountains of the French Riviera, can be handled on several levels. Each teaching can be worked with to whatever degree you select. You decide how far you want to take it. It is *your* quest, *your* journey. Travel it as you wish.

The activities in this book are your main trail. They will provide ample opportunities for you to exercise your spiritual muscles as the trail follows the terrain of your life.

We have made provision, however, for the adventurer who wants to explore an area off the main trail. So if you ever feel the need to take yourself a step beyond and have the time and willingness to stretch yourself a bit, you can venture into the activity called *Off the Main Trail.* Please note that these are purely optional activities.

THE PLAN

Now here's the plan. Read the Teaching in the Guidebook first and then its corresponding Adventure in this Activity Book—back and forth, back and forth, until you complete the entire process.

You will soon see that all Adventures in this Activity Book have certain activities in common:

Soul-Talk Each Adventure begins with *Soul-Talk.* This is a call to action which you'll be decreeing often for the duration of that particular chapter. Make it your constant companion. Repeat your *Soul-Talk* statement, silently or aloud, as many times a day as you can think of it.

In addition to speaking it, you'll be writing out

your *Soul-Talk* three times. This will serve to impress it on your memory and in your consciousness (which is your soul, hence the name *Soul-Talk*). But rather than writing the statement over and over quickly, as if it were a punitive exercise, write it slowly one time. Then stop, close your eyes, take a deep breath and be still for a short time, ten or fifteen seconds. Then write it again and follow with another deep breath and pause. When you are ready, write the statement a third time. This helps you to assimilate the very personal meaning which each *Soul-Talk* holds for you.

Soul-Thoughts After you have completed writing your *Soul-Talk*, close your eyes, become quiet, and allow whatever thoughts and feelings that have been generated to present themselves. Any impressions you have about the *Soul-Talk* or about any of the current teaching or any thoughts about *The Quest* should be noted here. *This is an extremely important section because it will become the log of your journey.*

The significance of this exercise cannot be over-emphasized. The more time you can spend with this Activity and the more honestly and accurately you can identify and express your feelings, the richer will be your experience.

Writing Thoughts and Feelings Do not miss any part of the journey, especially the writing assignments. Sometimes it might be tempting to skip over them, thinking that it's enough to answer the questions in your mind, but writing encourages you to focus your thoughts and, to more precisely, identify your feelings. They—your thoughts and your feelings—are the most important part of this Activity Book. Please don't feel limited by the amount of space we've given you to write out your responses. By all means, use additional paper if you need it.

Stepping-Stones   Each chapter ends with a task to perform: a simple change in life-style (a baby step) designed to help pave the way toward bigger changes.

It's not enough to _want_ to change. That's only the beginning. A desire without a deed is a dead end. After all, if we don't change something, how can we expect anything to change? The act of physically _doing_ something different every day rousts us out of our natural inclination to preserve the status quo.

You will notice that these _Stepping-Stones_ are not big changes. They are very simple changes of habits, attitudes, opinions, and reactions. But it is exactly these types of little changes that make the more important changes easier.

Look at it this way. If you change the speed, size, or direction of even the tiniest gear in a machine, _all_ gears are affected! Similarly, if you change the direction of even the tiniest habit, attitude, opinion, or reaction in your life, _all_ thoughts and actions will begin to change, and that's the magic of these _Stepping-Stones._ Whereas it's difficult to make the big changes that we all want to make (if they were easy, we would have made them long ago!); it's easy to make the small changes. And each small change acts like a stepping-stone, taking us further on the path of transformation.

Most of the _Stepping-Stones_ won't seem to tie in with the chapter they're in. You will notice this right away. Don't let it confuse you. In fact, only a very few _Stepping-Stones_ are designed specifically for particular chapters. This may seem haphazard, but we assure you it is not. These _Stepping-Stones_ have one purpose and one purpose only: They are designed to lead to change. *Change* is what *The Quest* is all about. The more changes you make in your life, the easier it is for your life to change.

You will also notice an almost childlike simplicity to these *Stepping-Stones*. That's because foundations are the first part of a building. Stone by stone you are creating a solid base, so it's important that you incorporate the *Stepping-Stones* into your daily behavior. Each *Stepping-Stone* assignment is to be used the entire time you are working on that Adventure.

A BRIEF SUMMARY

To briefly summarize how you will be proceeding in this Activity Book:

1. Read: After completing the Guidebook chapter, read the entire corresponding Adventure in this Activity Book, including the questions. Don't attempt to answer the questions at this time. Just get an overall flavor for the Adventure. (The logos will help you identify each Activity.)

2. Soul-Talk: Write the *Soul-Talk* three times, pausing between each time. Then use the phrase as many times a day as you can during the week.

3. Soul-Thoughts: After completing your *Soul-Talk* writing, allow time for your thoughts and feelings to clarify themselves and then write them down.

4. Activities: Follow the directions for each activity in order. Write your answers as thoroughly and completely as you can.

5. Option: Decide if you want to step *Off the Main Trail*. If you do, complete this Activity before going on to the next Adventure.

6. Stepping-Stone: Now is the time you want to

incorporate the *Stepping-Stone* into your daily schedule. It appears at the end of the chapter, but don't wait until then to use it. Start it after your first reading of the chapter.

PERSONAL PROGRAM

Whether you choose to make this great adventure alone or in a group, *The Quest* is your personal program. It is something you will be doing for yourself. It just might be the most important endeavor you will ever undertake.

You will be making the effort, but it will be *you* who reaps the benefits. Know that you deserve every bit of the good that lies ahead for you on the path.

_____

STARTING OVER

Don't lose your confidence if you slip,
  Be grateful for a pleasant trip,
And pick yourself up, dust yourself off,
  Start all over again.
—From the song "Pick Yourself Up"
  Dorothy Fields & Jerome Kern[1]

Is your life wonderful in every way? Are you experiencing absolute good in every area of your life?

"Who me? Are you kidding?"

Okay, then it's time to see what's getting in the way. Something's coming between God's desire for you (absolute good) and your willingness to accept that good.

Your willingness to allow that good to come into your life is the most important decision you will ever make. If you are serious about beginning *The Quest*, you have already made that decision. Now it's a matter of doing all you can to stay with it.

1. Copyright 1936, T. B. Harms Co., c/o The Welk Music Group, Santa Monica, Calif.

GETTING STARTED

You stand at an exciting spot, the junction of the familiar, strewn with worn-out ways, and the unfamiliar with all of its limitless possibilities.

Before venturing into any *terra incognita*, it's best to equip yourself with a compass. Let your *Soul-Talk* help steer you. Let it remind you that you can never run out of fresh starts. No matter what!

SOUL-TALK

 I'm at Possibility Junction.

Write this declaration three times, pausing between each line to allow the statement to saturate your consciousness. Then say it aloud or silently as many times as possible each day during this Adventure.

1. _____

2. _____

3. _____

SOUL-THOUGHTS

 After you have completed writing your *Soul-Talk*, take time to sit quietly and observe your thoughts and feelings. Write them down.

1. *Describe in detail the summons you heard which called you to your quest. Was it a specific dramatic event in your life, or was it a persistent inner urging? If it was a particular event, describe where you were when it took place. Describe your surroundings with as much detail as you can remember—the sights, the sounds, the smells. Were other people with you? What did they look like, and how did they act? Write this out.*

(A good way to do this is to sit quietly and relive the scene or the inner urgings which summoned you. It may take time, even several days, to crystallize your impressions. No need to rush. Your summons was a pivotal event in your life and is well worth spending some time on.)

2. *Is there more than one* terra incognita *in your life? What areas are as yet unexplored? Is there a relationship you are timid about reconciling, an addiction you are afraid you can't control, a physical problem you are reluctant to face?*

Where is the major terra incognita *in your life?*

What is the one area you are most afraid to explore? Be as specific as possible. Clue: This will be the area of your map with the most dragons. Identify this area now. (In the example referred to in the Guidebook, the *terra incognita* for the one sister was a commitment to graduate school.)

The terra incognita *in my life is* _____

_____

3. *What do you think are the dragons that keep you from venturing into these areas—the threatening creatures which prevent you from making a fresh start? In other words, what are you afraid of?* For instance, if the area is a relationship, perhaps you're afraid of being rejected. (You may feel that this is a lot for you to handle at this point in your quest, but give it a try.)

Terra Incognita	Dragons
Graduate school	Too old to begin again
	Too late to start a new career
	Too much discrimination against women in teaching
New relationship	Fear of rejection

4. *What rich resources do you suspect lie in this "new world"? What treasure will you discover when you enter this territory?* It could be that dealing with that relationship has the potential to give you an improved self-image. That would certainly be a worthwhile treasure.

A friend of ours finally found the courage (and the faith) to leave a boring job and start his own business. His discovered treasure? "For the first time in my life, I feel in charge." His new sense of freedom and satisfaction is something he formerly thought would never be his, but then he found out he could begin again.

Terra Incognita	Dragons	Treasure
Graduate school	Too old to begin again Too late to start a new career Discrimination against women	Feeling good about self Doing something I love Making better money

Terra Incognita	Dragons	Treasure
		More time with my children
New relationship	Fear of rejection	Improved self-image
		Loving partner
		Someone to share life with
New job	Fear of no income	Be my own boss
	Not sure I will succeed	Chance for more money
		More self-confidence

APART OR A PART?

Now let's explore your feelings about you and God within you. The Guidebook spoke about the difference between feeling *apart from* God and *a part of* God. If you are feeling apart from God, then you can only go as far as you humanly can take yourself. You are limited by what you think and feel and believe you are.

But if you know that you are part of God, then you are limited only by what you think God in you can do. And that, of course, has no limits.

5. *Are there any areas in your life that you really feel are a part of God? If so, write them here. And then identify in which area you feel a part of God most strongly.*

6. Your answers to the previous Activity give you a good indication of where to make your new beginnings. Keep your energies invested in the areas where you feel the connection with your divine Source. *List specific steps you can take to spend more time in these areas.*

PLANNING YOUR PLAN

You are going to need a good schedule to stoke the fire of your enthusiasm.

There are 48 Teachings designed for a one-year commitment. (Considering that life is eternal, a year is a blink of an eye.) Be realistic. Can you give yourself to God for a year? If, after this period of time, your life is not overflowing with a deeper sense of love and peace and joy, you can always return to your current way of life.

The best way to change your life is to make daily changes in your life. An enthusiastic fifty-two-week commitment to change is guaranteed to change you.

If you are working with a group, do your reading and writing assignments at home and then meet with the group once (or more) a week to discuss both the Guidebook and the activities.

OFF THE MAIN TRAIL

That completes the activities on the main trail. After having finished them, you may want to consider the following *Off the Main Trail* activity, which, of course, is optional. Attempt it only if you wish to take your journey a step beyond to stretch yourself a bit, to venture into new territory.

Here is your optional Activity for Adventure 1. Keep in mind that you can bypass it completely, or even attempt it at a later time if you wish.

If you are not a stranger to introspection, you might have a good idea where your dragons came from origi-nally. How did they get onto your map in the first place? Discuss this in as much detail as you feel comfortable with. (Use extra paper if necessary.)

STEPPING-STONE

Scrupulously follow your new schedule.

Try on your new schedule for size. Whatever schedule you eventually come up with is going to be with you for the next year. Follow it carefully this week, making sure it's realistic, that it works for you.

This is the week to make any changes in your schedule. It doesn't have to be carved in stone like the Ten Commandments, but it shouldn't be written in sand either. Alter it only when absolutely necessary and only after much consideration.

(You'll see that future *Stepping-Stones* are a bit more unconventional. But for this week, it's quite enough to experiment with your schedule and make sure it fits. It's got to be not only workable, but comfortable.)

You are at Possibility Junction.

*None is so rich as to throw
away a friend.*
            —Turkish Proverb

No one in the entire history of the universe was created exactly like you. Not only is your genetic code substantially different from everyone else's, but your thought patterns, your awareness, and your spiritual aspirations are absolutely unmatched. You are a one-of-a-kind, *bona fide*, original! As the old song says, "There will never be another you."

Yet with all your uniqueness, you are also a social creature who needs the support of others. You know this is true in an economic sense. (You can't be a doctor, lawyer, architect, butcher, baker, and candle-stick maker to yourself.) It's also true in a spiritual sense. You can grow best spiritually when you are surrounded by people who celebrate your spiritual journey.

It's time to start thinking of your life—the people

in your life, and all the activities in your life—in terms of a quest. Begin right now to observe how everything and everyone you encounter relates to your journey toward transformation, how they support it or hinder it.

Like the Guidebook analogy of a potted plant, it's good to think of yourself as someone who wants to grow and to look at the people in your life as part of the soil in which you're rooted.

SOUL-TALK

I have supportive friends.

1. _____

2. _____

3. _____

SOUL-THOUGHTS

Now is the time to check out your "soil" to see how conducive to your spiritual growth it is. Let's begin with your situation at home. Since this is where you probably spend most of your time, it has the most influence on your growth.

1. *Sit quietly and think about your home life. Don't try to analyze your feelings. Just gently become aware of them as you relax your body. Pay attention to the impressions you receive, objectively observing them as if you were a third party.*

2. *On a scale of 1 to 10 (ten being the best), how conducive is your present home life to sound spiritual growth?*

(If you answered 0, think again. There's always something that can help you in your quest, even if it's only the luxury of having a roof over your head when you pray!)

3. *What aspects of your home life are conducive to sound spiritual growth? List everything, including even the tiniest bit of help.* Consider the people as well as all other aspects, such as room arrangements, sounds, comfort, and so forth. Be specific. Take your time answering this.

4. *What specific steps can you take to make your home environment even more supportive of your spiritual growth?* This may mean rearranging rooms or schedules. It may mean changing TV watching habits. It may mean playing uplifting music.

5. *What aspects of your home life are* not *conducive to sound spiritual growth? Consider the same aspects as before.* Be specific and thorough.

6. *What specific steps can you take to avoid having these interfere with your spiritual growth?* Approach this from a new and positive angle. You might surprise yourself.

SPIRITUAL SUPPORT GROUP

Now, at the beginning of your quest, is the time to form your Spiritual Support Group if you are planning on having one.

Every support group has a positive energy. If you have ever been a part of a group dealing with weight loss or addiction or phobias or even a group formed to oppose a zoning change, you know how much energy it can generate. A group formed to support spiritual growth is infinitely more powerful because it taps into an energy from the Highest Source.

Your Spiritual Support Group could be with you for a long time, so *select it carefully*. Don't automatically assume all of your friends or family will make good Spiritual Support Group members. You may share at many wonderful and loving levels with them, but they may not share your spiritual aspirations right now.

The people you choose to accompany you on your quest will be one of your richest sources of spiritual support. They will celebrate with you on your peaks and encourage you in your valleys. For this reason, we emphasize the importance of supportive friends on *The Quest*.

How will you utilize your Spiritual Support Group? In many, many ways! The most valuable Spiritual Support Group is one you can take with you on *The Quest*—a sort of spiritual study group that meets on a regular basis to study the Guidebook and work on this Activity Book.

However, a study group is not essential. The relationship can be more casual than that. In fact, the friends who make up your Spiritual Support Group do not even have to live in the same town as you. They only have to be as close as a phone call.

If you are not meeting regularly with a Spiritual Support Group, you can still call on these friends individually when your motivation is sagging or your desire to continue your quest is wavering. Their love and support can be the difference in your continuing or quitting.

You can celebrate a new spiritual insight with members of your Spiritual Support Group and keep them abreast of your progress. The more you avail yourself of this support, the easier it is to stay on the path.

How many do you need for a Spiritual Support Group? Although we feel that three is really optimum, one spiritual friend (sort of a spiritual sponsor) can be enough.

7. *Write the names of all your friends who you feel would be understanding and supportive of your quest.* It may surprise you to realize that some of your best friends may not be good choices for your Spiritual Support Group. Maybe you share a lot with them socially and emotionally, but find that spiritually you are miles apart.

8. *From that list, choose one, two, or three friends who you feel will* totally *support you on your quest. Contact these friends (or friend) and ask them if they would be willing to support you.* If you're planning on having more than one person, approach each one individually. When the time feels right, explain exactly what you are doing and ask if he or she will actively support you.

Note: Your first reaction to this activity may be uneasiness. Sometimes we feel self-conscious about communicating with someone on deeper levels than we normally do. But if you will just bypass the outer layers and deal directly from your higher self to the other person's higher self, you will make the delightful discovery that he or she has the same inner feelings, the same longings, as you. It's such a relief to cut through all the superficial stuff and communicate directly from the heart.

9. *My Spiritual Support Group is:*

a. _____

b. _____

c. _____

You will find that *The Quest* is easily incorporated into a group project. And should it work out that your Spiritual Support Group can become your study group, that will be a real bonus. In any case, your friends will help you stay disciplined to *The Quest.*

Not only that, when you can feel that you're in a

safe environment surrounded by supportive people, your defenses and resistance will drop and there will be a shift toward wholeness and growth. When you feel safe, there is a natural tendency for healing to take place. Truly supportive friends make you feel safe. Cherish them.

OFF THE MAIN TRAIL

 Keep a journal every day this week. Divide each page into two columns: SUPPORTIVE and NON-SUPPORTIVE. Every major activity and personal inter-action of the day should be recorded in the appropriate column.

At the end of the week, you will have a clearer idea as to what will remain in your life and what must be de-emphasized.

SUPPORTIVE	NONSUPPORTIVE

STEPPING-STONE

Tell a friend why you like him or her.

Every day this week, call up a different friend and, in the course of your conversation, tell your friend exactly why you like him or her. If you run out of friends to compliment, tell acquaintances why you like them, tell co-workers why you enjoy working with them, tell your favorite store clerk why he or she is your favorite, compliment the mail carrier on doing a good job, write a letter of praise to your newspaper or a public official.

It doesn't really matter whom you tell. This *Stepping-Stone* is simply to share your light, to do something constructive that you don't normally do—and to do it every day.

You have supportive friends.

*W*HAT GOD IS

An atheist is a man who has
no invisible means of support.
　　　　　—John Buchan

"Faster than a speeding bullet, more powerful than a locomotive, able to leap tall buildings in a single bound. Look ... up in the sky. It's a bird ... It's a plane ... It's ..."

How easy to identify and define Superman. How impossible to define God.

But the fact that we can't define God doesn't mean we can't, at some level, "know" God, and the best way we can know God is through experiences that transform us. The more transformative the experience, it seems, the closer we can come to knowing God.

For example, people who have undergone "miraculous" healings have had profoundly powerful experiences of God. So often this entirely changes their lives. Yet just as a powerful healing of the body can lead to knowing God as life, the reverse is also true:

Spontaneous insights into God as life have led to miraculous healings.

Many people have experienced God as love. After opening themselves to the love of God within them, they can share this love with others when they were not able to do it before.

The same with peace. Letting go of the struggle to control an exasperating situation and letting God bring serenity may lead to a deep and genuine experience of God as peace.

SOUL-TALK

God is at work in my life.

1. _____

2. _____

3. _____

SOUL-THOUGHTS

While it is true that God cannot be defined, certain experiences can act like windows through which God becomes known to you in personal and powerful ways.

1. *What has been your single most profound experience of God at work in your life?* If you feel you have never had a profound God experience, write about someone you know or someone you've heard of who has had such an experience.

2. *When do you usually feel closest to God?* Is it when you are in a church or temple? When you pray? When you see a sunset? When you hear special music?

3. *When do you usually feel furthest from God?*

4. *What three words spontaneously come to mind when you think of God?*

a. _____

b. _____

c. _____

5. *Here are two quotes on the nature of God:*

a. *"The Universe is but one vast symbol of God."*

—Thomas Carlyle

b. *"The best way to know God is to love many things."* —Vincent van Gogh

Select one of these statements and explain what it means to you.

6. *How can you know God better?* As we move along in *The Quest*, you'll have more ideas about this, but write out your present ideas now.

7. *List three things which to you are evidence of God in your world.*

a. _____

b. _____

c. _____

OFF THE MAIN TRAIL

Thomas Troward, the British judge and metaphysician, often used the statement "Principle is not bound by precedent." Explain this concept, and discuss what it can mean to you personally.

STEPPING-STONE

First thing every morning, smile at yourself in the mirror.

Sound strange? Maybe so. Yet it's psychologically and physiologically sound.

Every morning, when you first see yourself in the mirror, *smile*. It may be a struggle, but give it a go! Look at yourself and smile, even if it takes pushing up the corners of your mouth with your fingers!

Although the great humorist W. C. Fields advised us to "Start every day off with a smile and get it over with," the truth is that a smile will set you up for a good day. It's a fact that you get happy when you see someone smile. It's an automatic response. Seeing a smiling face makes you happier, even if only on an unconscious level. (And there's an extra bonus: it causes the release of beneficial chemicals in your body, especially those that strengthen the immune system.)

Secondly, there's instant positive feedback to you. For example, what is the message someone is sending you when you see that person smile? "Everything's okay with me." Right? That's the message, that all is well in his or her life.

You'll get the same message about yourself. When you see yourself smile, no matter what's going on in your life, the unconscious message to yourself is, "Everything's okay with me."

Once your mind gets the idea that everything is all right, the body follows and moves toward physical and emotional healing. You're going to be amazed at how this simple little daily activity of smiling at yourself in the mirror will bring you so many far-reaching benefits.

Smiling at yourself first thing in the morning is a terrific way to begin again. In fact, every smile will be a new beginning!

PS: This is one Stepping-Stone *you shouldn't give up when you complete the lesson. Let this one become a lifetime habit.*

God is at work in your life.

Men go abroad to wonder at the heights of mountains, at the huge waves of the sea, at the long courses of the rivers, at the vast compass of the ocean, at the circular motions of the stars; and they pass by themselves without wondering.

—St. Augustine

Centuries ago, actors wore masks to indicate the roles they were playing. The mask was called a *persona.*

The word *persona* is still with us, but the mask has taken on a new meaning. It refers now to any "mask" we wear to show what "role" we are playing. We wear a mask of self-assurance when timidly applying for a new position, a mask of composure when actually upset about an insult, a mask of "I'm okay" when in fact hurt and disappointed over the end of a relationship. Anytime we wear a mask, anytime we play a role that's not authentic, anytime we feel the need to hide behind a mask of *who* we are, we hide (from ourselves and others) *what* we are.

The masks that we wear as we strut upon the stage of life tell our audience *who* we are. Actually, they proclaim who we *think* we are, which is as infinitely changeable as our thoughts and our reactions. But *what* we are can never change. God established that an eternity ago.

SOUL-TALK

I am God's child.

1. _____

2. _____

3. _____

SOUL-THOUGHTS

The distinction between *who* you are and *what* you are can help you get a much clearer picture of yourself and your life. Also, it can be a real help to you on your quest.

1. *Write down all of the titles that define* who *you are.* (For example: mother, father, sister, golfer, hunter, neighbor, Democrat, friend, dentist, employee, child, commuter, and so on.) Make an exhaustive list.

2. *Choose three of the titles that you feel* most *identify you.* (For example: mother, nurse, wife.)

a. _____

b. _____

c. _____

3. *Would the* essential *you be different if you were not these three things? Would it affect you at your essence? Explain your answer.* In other words, if one of the three titles you chose is your profession (let's say salesman), would it affect you *at your essence* if you changed careers and became an accountant?

Would it change what you are? Explain your answer.

JUST A HEAP OF CHEMICALS?

You are a walking, talking chemical compound! Your physical body is made up of about forty-two different elements. These are exactly the same elements that appear on the periodic table in any chemistry book and which are found throughout the physical universe. Yet if a similar ratio of the same forty-two elements which compose your physical body were mixed together, they could not walk and talk and think as you can.

4. *What is the difference between you and any other collection of these forty-two elements?*

5. *Why is* The Quest *referred to as a "journey of the soul"?*

OFF THE MAIN TRAIL

Spend one day this week being your true self. Each thought must be examined for love and kindness and understanding. Is it coming from your spiritual essence, or is it just one more of those old conditioned human mind patterns? Keep a particular monitor on your emotions. (This can be the most difficult part of the assignment.) Observe your feelings throughout the day, making adjustments as needed to keep yourself positive and loving.

Your actions will be the most obvious. Before doing anything, check to see if it will result in good for everyone concerned. Do you think your actions reflect God's will, or are they strictly your will?

Before you fall asleep each night, carefully evaluate the day. How authentic were you? How well did you express the *real* you?

This may not be an easy project. Most of us are so hidden under various masks and contrived actions that it takes effort to simply be ourselves. If you find you can't make it through one entire day without falling back into old patterns, that's okay. Try it again the next day. The toughest part of this may be simply *remembering* to do it.

(We cautioned you that these optional *Off the Main Trail* activities are for the adventurous, but if you can accomplish this one, the rewards will be extremely gratifying.)

STEPPING-STONE

Look directly into your eyes in a mirror every morning for one full minute.

If you are anything like us, you will feel self-conscious the first time you do this—but do it anyway. After all, when do you really see yourself? Yes, you look at your reflection when you shave or put on makeup or comb your hair, but are you really seeing yourself? You're in for quite an unusual experience if you look past *who* is peering back at you and try to discern just *what* is behind those eyes.

You are God's child.

One man was true to what is in you and me.
He saw that God incarnates himself in man.
                    —Ralph Waldo Emerson

It's not always easy to grasp the difference between "Jesus" and "Christ," but the distinction is absolutely crucial to understanding the nuances of what Jesus said about Himself and about God and about you! Without this clear distinction between Jesus and Christ, reading The Gospels doesn't supply us with the full nourishment of the words. It's like admiring the shiny skin on an apple and ignoring the nourishing fruit inside.

So, at the risk of overdoing it, let's review it one more time. Jesus is the person. Christ is not the person. Christ is a principle. Christ was not born in Bethlehem, Jesus was. Christ did not walk the earth, Jesus did. Christ did not preach and teach, Jesus did.

Conversely, when Paul said, "Christ in you, the hope of glory" (Col. 1:27), he wasn't referring to Jesus.

He was referring to the Christ principle in all people, the same Christ principle that Jesus had already discovered in Himself. (If this is still confusing, please reread Teaching 5 in the Guidebook again. This concept is so important that you should not go on to your next Adventure until this difference between "Jesus" and "Christ" is perfectly clear.)

SOUL-TALK

I allow the Christ to express Itself through me.

1. _____

2. _____

3. _____

SOUL-THOUGHTS

Knowing that someone very much like you overcame a great challenge makes it easier for you to believe that you can do it. As a trivial example, recall when, as a teenager, you took your driver's license examination. It looked formidable. But the realization that some of your friends had passed the test gave you confidence that you could pass it too. The fact that one human being, Jesus, found oneness with God should give you confidence that you, too, will find it.

Also, we have a book of instructions! Although Jesus Himself never wrote any of the Bible, His teachings and His example are well recorded. The Gospels are a veritable "how-to" on spiritual transformation. It's a matter of reading them and then doing what Jesus says.

Note: If you haven't read the four Gospels recently (Matthew, Mark, Luke, and John), we strongly recommend this as a good time to begin reading them again.

1. *What is the most human aspect of Jesus, the one with which you can most easily identify?* For example, He was told by His mother what to do at the Marriage Feast at Cana (Jn. 2:1-11). (We've all experienced something like that!) He showed anger at the money changers in the Temple (Mt. 21:12-13). (Who hasn't been angry?) He fell sound asleep in the boat after a long day of preaching (Mk. 4:35-40). (Ever done that after coming home from work?)

2. *What is the most attainable characteristic that*

Jesus has shown you? In other words, what virtue has He shown in His ministry on earth that you think you can incorporate into your life most easily? Love? Humility? Patience? Or some other virtue?

   3. *What* specific *steps can you take to incorporate this virtue into your life?* Remember to list *specific* actions you will take. It's not enough to say, "I'll be more humble." That's not specific enough. Better is, "I'll listen to my friends in the car pool instead of always telling them what I think." "I won't brag about my volunteer work" is another example of a specific action. Yes, these are small changes, but if you look at the foundation of your home, it's made up of many small bricks.

   4. *Which of the characteristics of Jesus that you admire is the most difficult for you to incorporate into your life?* For example, many people have trouble with patience. We live in a go-go world, and it's easy to get caught up in the rush.

5. *Why is this characteristic the most difficult for you to incorporate into your life?* Try to answer something more than, "I've always been that way." Staying with the characteristic of patience, your answer could be, "I've always had to feel that I'm in control. I get very stressed when things don't happen my way."

6. *What* specific *steps can you take to begin to bring that characteristic into your daily life?* Your answer might include meditating twenty minutes a day or avoiding those situations that stress you or doing some deep breathing every time you stop for a red light or simply becoming aware of your feelings.

7. *What is your interpretation of Jesus' words,*

"He who believes in me will also do the works that I do; and greater works than these will he do" (Jn. 14:12)?

 8. Okay. Here's the big one: *Explain who Jesus was.*

9. And here's the one you were hoping we wouldn't ask: *Explain what Christ is.*

10. *Now that you answered #8 and #9, explain how these two terms apply to you.*

OFF THE MAIN TRAIL

The same Christ essence which is in you is also in every other human being. In special moments, we catch glimpses of the Christ in another person: we connect Christ-to-Christ for a brief second or two, beyond time and beyond physical space in a fleeting touch with oneness. This is the "I and Thou" experience which theologian Martin Buber described in his profound book of the same title.

Select one person to whom you find it difficult to relate. This can be a relative, an acquaintance, or even a stranger whom, for some reason, you are offended or repulsed by. (Possibly, someone already springs to mind.) Arrange to be in that person's presence, at a distance of six feet or less, for as long as it takes you to see the Christ behind his or her eyes.

Lift your awareness above your surroundings, beyond any conversation, beyond the appearance and behavior of this person. Bypass all of the outer and go directly from your Christ to his or hers. Feel the connection, the knowing. You may not be able to hold this connection more than a few seconds, but you both will have felt the presence of the Christ.

If you are especially adventurous, you can do this as often as you wish. You'll love it.

STEPPING-STONE

Incorporate your answer to #6 into every aspect of your life this week.

Take the specific actions that you named in answer #6 and, to the best of your ability, consciously apply them at work and at home. If, for example, you chose "patience," then consciously practice patience with your children, mate, fellow employees, boss, and friends. Practice it while you wait at the supermarket or at the post office. Use it while waiting in line when you're in a hurry. Consciously do this. The key word is *consciously.* Be aware that you are changing your behavior.

You allow the Christ to express Itself through you.

*Most people are bothered by those passages
of Scripture they do not understand, but the
passages that bother me are those I do
understand.*

—Mark Twain

The Bible can become a very personal teacher to
you, a real "one-on-one" experience, if you want it to
be.

From this point on, you will be looking to the
Scriptures for new insights into your life. You will
discover that so many times, when you metaphysically
interpret a story, you'll end up having one of those
"Aha!" experiences.

Viewed this way, the Scriptures actually become
exciting, insightful, alive, and even—dare we say it?—
fun! And since you are always changing, the metaphysical meanings you glean from Bible stories will
change too. What a story represents to you today
might not apply at another time. That's why *you* are
the best interpreter for *you.*

SOUL-TALK

 I am open to new insights.

1. _____

2. _____

3. _____

_____

SOUL-THOUGHTS

1. *Now take out your Bible. (We prefer to use the Revised Standard Version.) You'll need it, along with a quiet place and a quiet time. Read the story of David and Goliath in 1 Samuel 17:4-51. Read it all the way through as you would an adventure story.*

2. *Sit quietly for a few minutes and allow the story line to settle in.*

3. *Now read it again, but this time be aware of all the characters and symbols (David, Goliath, Saul, the Philistines, the valley, the mountains, and so on). Don't try to interpret them as you read, but be open to any feelings you may spontaneously receive.*

4. To help you get your feet wet, we've made a list of some of the characters, events, and symbols of the story. *Quietly open yourself now to what these things mean to you. What part of you or what part of your life do they represent? After each item, write one or two sentences that express your gut feelings about each.* Don't intellectualize or try to reason it out logically. Go with your feelings. If nothing comes to you immediately, go to the next one.

David _____

_____

Goliath _____

_____

Israelites _____

_____

Philistines _____

_____

Valley _____

_____

Mountains _____

_____

Saul _____

_____

Armor _____

_____

Goliath's weapons _____

_____

_____

A POSSIBLE INTERPRETATION

(We're going to give you our interpretation of this rich story now. It's not the right one, because there are no "right" and "wrong" interpretations. There is only what's right or wrong for you. But we're doing this to show you how you can get started on your own interpretations.)

The story of David and Goliath is much more than a simple adventure story about putting your faith in God. Yes, that certainly is the basic message, but there are many other messages.

You can personalize the story and see that "Goliath" is that huge problem looming menacingly in your life, threatening you, bullying you. Maybe your giant is the severe arthritis that you've been told is incurable or the dead-end job that pays so little, but you can't leave because you don't have enough education or the child of yours caught up in the drug culture. Like Goliath, every day it comes to the *valley*, a low state of consciousness, to remind you that it's still there. Like the Children of Israel, you may fear it. You may even be afraid to fight it because it looks so over-powering. Goliath is almost 10 feet tall with *armor* that weighs 150 pounds and a *spearhead* that weighs 18 pounds. But can you see that these could represent some "facts" about your problem: the medical reports, the personnel manager's opinion, the statistics on recovery from drug abuse?

Goliath constantly challenges the Israelites on the mountain, and they are fear-filled. You, of course, are the Israelites. And surely the "Philistines," jeering on the other side of the mountain, represent news stories, friends, and society in general—but mostly parts of you—that chide, "You don't stand a chance against your problem."

Then here comes David, who believes he can kill the giant. But he's not a warrior. He's a peaceful shepherd. He represents the spiritual part of you. "David" is that part of you which can deal with a problem from a higher level. Notice that David doesn't face Goliath on Goliath's terms. When Saul dresses him in his armor, David takes it off.

Who is Saul? Could he be the part of you that wants to turn things over to God but can't quite let go? ("Your will, God, but let me give You some advice on how to go about it! I'll use my old armor, just in case.") But David refuses to use Saul's weapons. He knows no one can beat Goliath on Goliath's terms. Goliath is huge, a mighty and unbeatable foe.

So instead of trying to fight Goliath on Goliath's terms, David asserts, "You come to me with a sword and with a spear and with a javelin; but I come to you in the name of the Lord of hosts ... whom you have defied. This day the Lord will deliver you into my hand" (1 Sam. 17:45-46).

Think of it. Here's a young shepherd boy telling the giant, who has the entire Israeli army quaking with fear, just what he's going to do to him! David has *chutzpah*, there's no denying that. But more importantly, he's an example of dealing with a serious problem on a higher level! He knows there are many problems that could defeat him but that no problem can defeat God.

There's our message, loud and clear: God first! In your own case, maybe you've done all you humanly can do for your healing, for your prosperity, for your anxiety over a loved one. Maybe you've been fighting the battle on Goliath's terms. If so, maybe now is the time to let go and let God take over.

Goliath's power rests completely in his enormous ability to instill fear. (Sound like anything in your life?) But David is not afraid of Goliath. In protecting his sheep, he had fought and defeated dangerous animals before. He knows God's will has to triumph if he trusts God: "The Lord who delivered me from the paw of the lion and from the paw of the bear, will deliver me from the hand of this Philistine" (1 Samuel 17:37). In other words, he accepts victory as a natural outcome of relying on God.

So he faces Goliath and what does Goliath do? He curses and threatens David once more. We interpret this as the problem's last ditch effort as you face it armed only with faith in God. It may seem to grow larger and more threatening as you start putting down your defenses and trusting God.

As Goliath approaches David, the boy "ran

quickly" to meet him. Isn't this a perfect example of faith? David doesn't stand still, he doesn't back up. He runs quickly *toward* Goliath. And then he takes action, he "puts feet on his prayers." He throws his stone and hits Goliath smack in the middle of the forehead, right in the intellect!

How does this relate to you? It's the intellect in you that keeps insisting that something is incurable or unachievable or impossible. When David cuts off the head of Goliath, when he removes the intellect entirely, the Philistine army takes to the hills. And so will all of the naysayers within your consciousness when you rely on the Christ within instead of trying to do it yourself. If you realize that your best thinking got you where you are (not a very cheerful thought!), it becomes easier to turn over your problem to God.

5. *As a little exercise, try to identify the "Goliath" in your life. If you can do this, write it down now.*

6. If you answered #5, you might want to give this a try. *Get yourself quiet again and project a picture in your mind's eye of this problem. See that ugly giant. Hear it bellowing. Hear the "Philistines" telling you that you can't do anything about it. What is the ugly giant shouting? What are the Philistines murmuring?* Don't intellectualize. Listen with your feeling nature.

Write it all down.

7. Let's do another story. This one is not as complex. It's the incident of Jesus' visit to his hometown. *Read Matthew 13:53-58. Read it as a story. Don't try to analyze it. Do this now.*

8. *Relax, sit quietly, and think about the story. Allow yourself to entertain any thoughts which pop into your mind. Don't ignore your instincts as to the meaning of the story.*

9. *Look at the scriptural passages again, making a list of the factors and characters contained in it. Then write what each one represents in you.*

Hint: Most people, when they first start interpreting metaphysically, make the mistake of letting the different characters represent things in general. For instance, in the David and Goliath story, they might say David represents a spiritually attuned person or the Philistines represent negative people. But this is not the way to do it. Each character and element in the story has to represent something in *you*. That's why we say the Bible is so personal. It speaks to *you*. David is *your* spiritual nature. The Philistines are *your* doubting, pessimistic thoughts. Clearer?

HOW DID YOU DO?

Did you feel the hometown represents your past, all the things which brought you to where you are now? Is it the part of you which believes you to be a certain way?

What about the character of Jesus? He usually represents your Christ self. Maybe you thought of Him here as "my Christ self which must rise up in the midst of this mess and claim my divine nature." The taunting townsfolk might symbolize your old self—your old way, your old thoughts about yourself—returning to confront you and challenge your new spiritual growth.

10. Let's do one more together. This time we'll go to the Old Testament. *Read Genesis 11:1-9, the allegory of the Tower of Babel.*

11. *Go over the story again in your mind and then make a list of the elements. After each one, write what it represents in you.*

We feel comfortable interpreting the Tower as our ego trying to make a name for itself. It was an attempt to reach heaven (a spiritual consciousness), but any spiritual project built solely of material things is doomed. The Tower of Babel might represent our own efforts to flourish without God, to serve ourselves only. The result is confusion and an inability to truly understand or relate to others.

Make sense? Did you come up with anything

similar? If not, don't worry. Remember, it's all very individual. With a little more practice, you'll soon get the hang of it. (You'll probably catch yourself metaphysically interpreting characters and events in books, movies, and even real-life situations!)

Translating the Bible into personal meaning for you becomes easier and easier with practice. Always remind yourself of two very important things:

a. The elements of a story always represent aspects of yourself.

b. There's no such thing as a right or wrong metaphysical interpretation. It's an absolutely individual meaning, uniquely yours.

Using metaphysical interpretations, you can read the Bible regularly for inspiration and personal illumination. There's no end to the discoveries you can make when you understand the Scriptures in this way.

OFF THE MAIN TRAIL

See what you can do with Acts 9:1-23. Read it carefully, think about it, read it again, and then let your subconscious play around with it for a while. Allow your emotions to get involved. When you're ready, write several paragraphs on how it relates to you. Be sure to include your emotional response.

STEPPING-STONE

Get your news from another source.

Look at or listen to a different news program. Or read a newspaper or newsmagazine that has a political or social point of view different from yours. This entire week take a look at current events with different "eyes and ears."

You are open to new insights.

ONENESS

*On this shrunken globe, men can no longer
live as strangers.*
                        —Adlai E. Stevenson

Consider your friends and acquaintances. Consider the people to whom you are attracted. They are probably as diverse as the colors in a meadow of wildflowers. Yet somehow, on some level, you have "connected" with them. There is an axiom in geometry which declares that things that are equal to the same thing are equal to each other. On the level of your attraction to these people in your life, there is an equality ... a sameness ... a oneness.

God exists in everything, albeit in a unique way. God, the Creator, is part of the common fabric of all creation, from the smallest atom in a butterfly to the farthest star. But it is the Christ in each human being that is the *specific* thread which joins humanity into a patchwork quilt of oneness.

SOUL-TALK

   I am one with all.

1. _____

2. _____

3. _____

_____

SOUL-THOUGHTS

If each of us is a unique expression of God, then each of us is one with the One. Isn't each drop of ocean water part of the vast ocean? All drops are one with the one ocean, so that makes all drops part of each other. Each drop can truly say, "I and the ocean are one."

1. *How are you different from your best friend?* (Write down any and all differences: physical, emotional, social, educational, political, and so forth.)

2. *Why is this person your best friend?* You probably noted many differences. If you're so different, why are you friends?

3. *How is your friend unique among all the people you know?* What characteristic or combination of

characteristics does he or she have that no one else
has?

4. *How are you unique?* What characteristic or
combination of characteristics do you have that no one
else has?

5. *What current news story is a good example of
how the news media exaggerate our human differences? In what way or ways does the media exaggerate our differences?*

6. What current news story is a good example of showing our oneness? Explain how this story illustrates our oneness.

7. The entire universe is connected, and you are part of it all. Everything is related to everything and to you. We have friends in northern California who say they feel this sense of oneness when they hug a red-wood tree. Another friend feels it when he bodysurfs ocean waves. Someone we know tells us his greatest sense of oneness with all life comes when he stares into the eyes of animals. Others feel it just being out in nature or seeing a beautiful sunset.

When do you sense your oneness the most? If it is practical, go to the place where it happens for you. If you can't physically get there, go in your imagination. Write a paragraph or two on what you feel and why you feel it.

"Nations will forget to fight if we continue to know that all people express the one life."

These are the words of Myrtle Fillmore, co-founder of the Unity movement. *What is your opinion of her statement? What does any conflict, from global war to an argument with a salesperson, say about our feelings of oneness?*

Write a few paragraphs expressing your ideas about the above question. Include any suggestions you have for helping the world to recognize its oneness.

Give a compliment to someone you don't like.

At least once a day every day this week seek out someone you've been having trouble liking and give him or her a compliment. It's okay if the compliment is simple. You may feel comfortable going only as far as saying, "I like your tie" or "I like the way you wear your hair." If it's complimentary, say it—and as you say it, mean it.

You are one with all.

CAUSE AND EFFECT

*We make our own fortunes and we call
them fate.*
                    —Benjamin Disraeli

How would you like to play a card game where
sometimes three-of-a-kind would beat a pair and other
times it wouldn't, sometimes the high card would win
and other times it wouldn't, sometimes you could keep
your cards hidden and sometimes you had to show
them to the other players?

That wouldn't make for a fun game because the
players would never know what to expect. How much
more fun it is to play Bridge or Gin Rummy or Poker or
Hearts or even Old Maid knowing there are rules, and
knowing you can plan your strategy within the rules.
The rules then become your ally because you always
have an idea of what your actions will bring.

How awful life would be if the "rules" kept changing. If you were loving to someone, you would be rewarded sometimes and punished other times. If you

were cruel to others, you would be rewarded or punished according to the caprice of the Rulemaker. Life
would turn into a dice game instead of an orderly,
rational, and eminently fair adventure, one over which
you can have control.

The fact that the Universal Creative Force gave us
free will means that we have a choice as to the means
of making our lives happy or unhappy. The choice is
ours. We decide every day when we wake up which it
will be, and we redecide at every now moment.

SOUL-TALK

I make my own world.

1. _____

2. _____

3. _____

SOUL-THOUGHTS

THE LAW AT WORK IN YOUR LIFE

Psychological counseling is nothing more than identifying causes of disharmony, helping to terminate them, and then putting new causes into motion. There are times when we are so enmeshed in these causes that we can't identify them. That's when a friend or counselor can be of great help. But often we can discover the cause of our trouble by the effect it is having on our lives. Remember, if your actions in the past have been the cause of an effect you don't like, you can put a new cause into motion.

1. *List three examples in your life when the law of cause and effect was obvious and immediate* (e.g., drank hot soup and burned my tongue, exercised and felt tired, jammed on the brakes and avoided a collision).

a. _____

b. _____

c. _____

2. *List three examples in your life where the law took longer to unfold* (e.g., studied hard and passed the exam, planted marigold seeds and got marigolds, purchased a certificate of deposit and six months later

collected interest).

a. _____

b. _____

c. _____

3. *Cite one example in your life where there were many years between cause and effect* (e.g., the rearing of your children, investing in a pension plan and retiring with good income, planting a peach pit and getting peaches off the tree).

HIDDEN HARVESTS

You don't always reap where you sow. Although you may perform a "good" or "bad" deed, you are seldom instantly rewarded or punished in kind. Unlike the immediate reward of cool, juicy sweetness from a chilled piece of watermelon or the immediate punishment of intense pain from touching a hot iron, life's rewards and punishments are usually far more subtle.

4. *Has it ever seemed to you that someone was not punished for doing something "bad"?* There are some real villains in history that may fit into this category, or you may have a personal example. *Write a few thoughts on this seeming inconsistency.*

5. There's a rather funny expression: "No good deed ever goes unpunished." It refers to the times we do something nice for someone, but we end up getting hurt or disappointed as a result. For example, you go to a great deal of trouble to set up an appointment with your dentist for a friend who has an emergency need, and the friend ends up hating the dentist and blaming you for a bad experience. *Is there something "good" you are doing that you feel is not being justly rewarded? Discuss this seeming inconsistency.*

6. *In Activity 2 of the first Adventure, you noted what new territory you wanted to explore. What specific cause can you now put into motion that will help to bring this about? Be sure to be specific.*

OFF THE MAIN TRAIL

Let one day this week be your day to set your new cause (see Activity 6) into motion. Make a point of lining up and then implementing a series of things you can do to support this cause. Try to make all your decisions and actions point toward the cause. Pay special attention to your thoughts and feelings as well.

STEPPING-STONE

Give someone a small gift.

Every day, give someone something nice. If you have to shop long and hard to purchase the gift, you're doing it wrong. The gift should be a small one—a pen someone may have admired, a flower, a box of cookies, even a magazine would do. If it's a gift you think the person will appreciate, give it.

You make your own world.

$\mathcal{H}$EAVEN AND HELL

I don't like to commit myself about heaven and hell—you see, I have friends in both places.

—Mark Twain

The great humorist was always ready with a quick quip. While it wouldn't have gotten a laugh, it would have been more accurate if Mark Twain had said, "I have friends with both attitudes," because heaven and hell, as we have seen, are states of mind. Beliefs about ourselves, feelings about what we deserve—these are the things that eventually show up as the circumstances of our lives, creating our personal heavens or hells.

What's even more important is that these attitudes about heaven and hell reflect our beliefs about God. They indicate to us what we think God is. For example, if we believe that God's desire for us is absolute good, can we possibly believe that God created a place of eternal damnation? Okay, so maybe you believe that some form of punishment is often needed to change behavior, but *eternal* damnation? That's pretty permanent. If one's idea of God were a God of love, he would be hard-pressed to believe in this kind of hell.

By dwelling on an "afterlife," it's easy to forget that today is the afterlife of yesterday. Your thoughts, feelings, and actions of yesterday are affecting you today. You've set up your own heaven or hell and are living in it now. No one sends you to heaven or to hell on a day of judgment. It is you who decides *if* and *when* and *where* you go and *how long you stay.*

SOUL-TALK

I have a heaven-state-of-mind.

1. _____

2. _____

3. _____

SOUL-THOUGHTS

Ideas about heaven and hell that you learned as a child have had a great impact on your thoughts and beliefs today. It's important for you to come to terms with these two subjects, to be at peace with what they are. Blindly following someone else's thinking implanted into your mind at an early age can be dangerous and undependable. If the motivation for your actions is fear of a punishment or anticipation of a reward that came from someone else's consciousness, then you may be living an inauthentic life.

It's time to examine your thoughts about heaven and hell. Are they still old thoughts passed along to you by someone else and never challenged by you, or are they revised according to your current feelings?

WHAT IS HELL?

The fear of being thrown into such a hideous place as hell after this lifetime has kept many people on the straight and narrow. No doubt about that. The stronger the belief in the punishment of eternal fires, the stronger the motivation to stay out of it. Let's face it, fear is a powerful motivator.

1. *Name three instances where you did not do something because of fear of punishment.* For example, you may not have driven through a stop sign only

because a police car was behind you. Or perhaps you were angry at your boss but didn't show your anger only because you were afraid he'd fire you.

2. *Name three instances where you performed a "good" deed because you feared the punishment if you did not perform it.* An example of this could be when as a child you visited your sick Aunt Milly only because your mother insisted.

3. *Do you think that doing "good deeds" because of fear brings the same sense of satisfaction or other rewards as "good deeds" done out of love? Explain your answer.*

4. *What is your earliest belief about hell?* In other words, describe the hell you grew up believing in. Was it a hell of fire and brimstone? Was it a hell where devils jabbed you with pitchforks? Be as descriptive as you can.

5. *Is your present belief about hell different? Explain the difference.* Compare your belief today with the belief described in the previous answer.

6. *What is the closest you have felt to a "hell on earth"? Describe it in detail.* Soldiers often refer to war as "hell on earth." Drug addicts think of their years of addiction as "hell." Some people refer to their former marriages as "sheer hell." It may be tempting to *dwell*

on the details of that time in your life. Don't fall for the temptation. The purpose of this question is not to get you emotionally caught up in old "tapes." It's to determine if a type of hell really can exist on earth. So describe it, then let it go.

7. It's been said that those who refuse to learn from the past are doomed to repeat it. *What have you learned from the "hell" in your past that will keep you from repeating it in the future?*

WHAT IS HEAVEN?

If you can't find heaven on earth right now, surely you can locate enough pieces of it from your past to make you hungry for more.

8. *Name three instances where you performed a "good deed" strictly because of the reward you thought you would receive.* For example, "I asked my boss and his wife to come over for dinner." Granted, feeding two people is a nice thing to do but was that really the motivation? Or, "I gave to a charity because my neighbor was collecting, and I was embarrassed not to give." We've all done good deeds for reasons other than what may have appeared on the surface.

9. *Name three instances where you performed a "good" deed strictly out of love, with no thought of any*

reward. "I helped prepare a Christmas dinner for a shelter for the homeless." Take your time with this. The feelings attached to your memories will guide you.

10. *What is your earliest belief about heaven?* Were there harps and angels and streets paved with gold? *Describe it.*

11. *Is your present belief about heaven different? Explain the difference.*

12. *What is the closest you have felt to a "heaven on earth"? Describe it in detail.* To some people, the feeling of being in love for the first time is "heaven." To others, heaven is the birth of their first child. Sometimes an unforgettable vacation is "heaven on earth."

13. *Compare the concept of "judgment day" covered in this teaching of the* Guidebook *to the concept of "Possibility Junction" mentioned in the first Teaching.* You're on your own with this one.

OFF THE MAIN TRAIL

You'll be exploring the four Gospels (Matthew, Mark, Luke, and John) for this sojourn. With the aid of a Bible concordance, locate, read, and list all of the thirty-two references which Jesus made to the "kingdom of heaven." Which is the one you relate to most? Why?

1. _____
2. _____
3. _____
4. _____
5. _____
6. _____
7. _____
8. _____
9. _____
10. _____
11. _____

12. _____
13. _____
14. _____
15. _____
16. _____
17. _____
18. _____
19. _____
20. _____
21. _____
22. _____

23. _____   28. _____

24. _____   29. _____

25. _____   30. _____

26. _____   31. _____

27. _____   32. _____

STEPPING-STONE

Share a funny cartoon.

The comic section of the daily newspapers is filled with cartoons. Snip out your favorite cartoon each day this week and share it with as many people as you can.

You have a heaven-state-of-mind.

GOOD AND EVIL

*For there is nothing either good or
bad, but thinking makes it so.*
        —Shakespeare, *Hamlet*

The fans were going wild! First one side screamed and cheered as the red team scored. Then the other side yelled and hollered as the blue team pulled ahead. Back and forth it went until finally, just before the buzzer sounded, the blue team scored the game-winning goal. The basketball game was over.

Bedlam broke out among the blue fans. Running out on the court to mob their team, they jumped up and down, laughing and hugging each other.

On the red side? Silence, sadness, and a few tears. The players sat on the bench, heads hanging down in utter dejection.

Was the outcome of the basketball game good or bad? That depended, didn't it? It depended on whether you were wearing red or blue. In actuality, the outcome of the game was neutral. It was neither good nor bad, *but thinking made it so.*

EVENTS ARE NEUTRAL

The fact is that all events are neutral. If they weren't, then all people would have exactly the same feelings, felt with exactly the same intensity, about all events. But they don't.

For example, a loved one's death may elicit the remark, "Oh, this is terrible news. What am I going to do without him?" An acquaintance may respond with, "Too bad. He was a nice guy." A stranger's reaction might be, "Oh, really? I didn't know the man." And someone who never did like the deceased person may crack, "That's good news. He deserved it."

So, what was the truth about the event of this man's death? It was neither good nor bad, *but thinking made it so.*

SOUL-TALK

 I walk the high road.

1. _____

2. _____

3. _____

SOUL-THOUGHTS

1. *Can you think of some events that you considered "bad" when they happened that you now see as
"neutral" or even "good"?*   Maybe there was a sporting
event like the game described above. Most of us have
cheered for a home team or a school team, only to be
saddened when they lost a big game. Some of us have
experienced unrequited love that was a "tragedy" when
it happened, especially when we were teenagers, but
which eventually moved into the "neutral" category.
(In fact, our misplaced youthful passion often gives us
a laugh when we think of it now.)

*Recount three such "bad" incidents that you now
view differently. Contrast your feelings at the times the
events took place with your feelings about those same
events now.*

CHECKING THE GAUGE

The Guidebook speaks about a "built-in gauge" which helps us keep our spiritual bearings and gives us direction in our daily decisions. The problem is that we don't always read the gauge. And, even when we do, we don't always pay attention to it.

How well do you think you watch your gauge? Answering the questions in this chapter will give you a good indication.

2. The Guidebook talks about the "high road" and the "low road." As you know, these are names for doing the "wrong" thing and doing the "right" thing. Most of us have traveled both roads. Right now get in touch with what each road feels like, so that you'll have less trouble recognizing whichever one you're on. *What feelings do you get when you're traveling the "low road," when you do something that you know is wrong or "bad"?* Do you get jumpy or stressed out? Are they visceral feelings? Are they nervous feelings? *Describe them.*

3. Describe one time in your life when you got those "low road" feelings very strongly.

4. What feelings do you get when you're traveling the "high road," when you do something that you know is right or "good"? Describe them.

5. Describe one time in your life when you got those "high road" feelings very strongly.

CHECK OUT THE SHADOWS

Look around you right now. Are there shadows in the room? Any under a table or a chair? What's causing them? Obviously, something is blocking the light. What would happen if you were to shine a bright light directly on those shadows? Would they disappear?

Now think about the darkest shadow in your life. Whatever area it is—ill health, anxiety over someone, fear, and so forth—let's see what bright light you can turn on that will disperse the darkness.

6. *Sit quietly and take a look at your present challenge. Don't react to it as you normally do. Just observe it as you would observe a shadow cast by anything whose light is blocked. Give your mind free rein to picture this shadow in any way it desires. When you have a clear picture of this shadow, gently envision a dimly lit floodlight directly above the shadow. Slowly turn up the power until the entire area that was dark is now bathed in brilliant light.* Don't go on to the next activity until you do this. When the area is bright and the shadow gone, you can continue.

7. Where did the shadow go? Has it completely vanished or is it back in your mind again? If it is, if you brought it back into your mind, then you can get it out of your mind. It has no power of its own. No Super Glue is holding it there. *Why do you think you are allowing this dark thought to live in your mind rent free?*

Perhaps it's been living there so long that it's become a habit.

Write out your opinion now.

IDENTIFYING WITH THE GOOD

We defined "evil" as anything which moves you away from a sense of the presence of God. "Good" was defined as anything which helps you feel your connection with God.

8. *What single thing, more than any other, moves you away from the awareness of the presence of God?* Is it a person? Is there someone in your life who pushes a button in you so that you respond in a negative way? Is there a situation that does the same thing? What moves you away from feelings of oneness with God?

9. *How can you get back in charge and stop moving away from the awareness of God?* Can you avoid the person? Can you change the situation? *What specific steps can you take to stop moving away from sensing the presence of God?*

Note: Please note that word *specific*. If you're going to change your life, you have to take some specific actions. It's not enough to say, "I'll try harder" or "I'll work at being better." Be explicit. What *exactly* will you do?

10. *What helps you feel your connection with God?* Again, this may be a person, or maybe it's an event or an inspiring location. You'll probably be able to think of several things. Whatever they are, list as many as you can.

11. *What can you do to spend more time with this person (or persons)? What can you do to spend more time enjoying these places and things? As always, be specific.*

Key: God is the force of good that powers this universe. We succeed or fail to the extent that we cooperate with this force. When we cooperate, we experience "good." When we fail to cooperate, we experience "evil."

OFF THE MAIN TRAIL

If you decide to venture onto this little path, be prepared for a workout. This one is quite a side trip, so take along a good supply of patience and intuition. The terrain is rough and not clearly marked.

Read The Book of Job, preferably using the Revised Standard Version of the Bible. A supplementary reading of the story in the Living Bible may broaden your comprehension.

Write a short essay on why you think Job suffered so. Was he "good" or was he "bad"? What, do you suppose, is the purpose of the book? What special insights did you receive about why the "righteous" suffer? Include any feelings and opinions you have about the story.

STEPPING-STONE

 Change the location of something in your house every day.

Remember the purpose of *The Quest*: changing you. This simple *Stepping-Stone*, like all *Stepping-Stones*, is designed to accustom you to change.

We're not talking about big changes here. No need to move your refrigerator into your bedroom or put your sofa in the shower. It's quite enough to change the location of your favorite vase or move your toaster to a different location on the counter. Any small change each day will work.

You walk the high road.

*In the event of a tornado, the Supreme Court
ruling against prayer in school will be temporarily
suspended.*

—Sign on a Nebraska high school

"God bless Mommy and Daddy, sister, brother, and Snoopy." We began with simple prayers.

It wasn't long before we prayed for "a new wagon and roller skates." Next, it was the boy who sat next to us in class: "Please, God, let him like me." Then, as life took on more serious overtones, our prayers reflected larger worries: "God, please make me well" and, "Please, God, make my son stop using drugs."

The most natural thing to do in times of concern is to pray. Why? Because it feels good! It feels right.

As we know, however, the purpose of prayer is not to give God a shopping list of things we want done for us. This kind of praying is best left in our childhood. The purpose of prayer is to help us know God and to allow God's will to be played out in our lives. We pray not to fill an earthly need but to satisfy the natural longing in our souls to know our true identity and to experience our Creator.

SOUL-TALK

God answers my prayers.

1. _____

2. _____

3. _____

SOUL-THOUGHTS

A MODEL PRAYER

What have you been praying for? It may be

something specific like a healing of your body or it may be a prayer for prosperity or of help for a loved one. Whatever it is, do you pray for it with the awareness that it is God's will for you?

The story of Lazarus is an outline of "how to pray." (As we review the story, note particularly Jesus' words. Also, recalling Teaching 6 about interpreting the Bible personally, here's a good opportunity to make this story meaningful in your life.)

THE STORY

Lazarus of Bethany and his sisters, Mary and Martha, were good friends of Jesus. Jesus was far away from Bethany when He was told that Lazarus was ill. So strong was His faith in God that He showed no concern for what others recognized as a terminal condition. In fact, He took His time going to Bethany. By the time He got there, Lazarus had been dead for four days! Anyone else would have no doubt felt that was that. But not Jesus. He went to the tomb and commanded them to "take away the stone." And then, "Jesus lifted up his eyes and said, 'Father, I thank thee that thou hast heard me. I knew that thou hearest me always.' " After saying this, "he cried with a loud voice, 'Lazarus, come out.' " And, indeed, Lazarus did come forth. At this point, Jesus ordered the astonished group to "unbind him, and let him go" (Jn. 11:1-44).

This, dear friend, is how to pray.

PRAYER STEPS

Let's look at what this story tells us about prayer and see how we can incorporate these same guidelines into our prayers. These are not hard-and-fast rules

101

chiseled in stone, but they worked well for Jesus. Since He is the Trailblazer on our quest, whom better to follow? These guidelines can help you, if you've been feeling your prayers are scattered or ineffectual.

Step I ... *Pray Believing:* There's little doubt that on a human level Jesus wanted His friend to be well. After all, He loved Lazarus and his sisters. Yet His comments indicated that He didn't see Lazarus' sickness as a problem. In fact, so centered was He in the knowledge that God's will was best for Lazarus, that He even took His time getting to Bethany.

Jesus' approach, before He even began to pray, was one of unshakeable belief. The attitude which you bring to your own prayers should also reflect that same kind of faith that everything's going to be okay.

Step II ... *Become Your Prayer:* "Take away the stone." In other words, take action. *Do something!* What an important step. Work to make your life congruent with your prayers. For example, are you praying for health but constantly talking about sickness (yours or anyone else's)? Are you eating the wrong foods, avoiding exercising, or not taking your medication? If you are, what is your life prayer?

Are you praying for your daughter but taking every opportunity to tell people how worried you are about her and what you are afraid will happen to her? Is your every thought of her a fear-filled one? Then what is your life prayer?

Take a careful, objective look at your life prayer, because *that's* what you're asking for. Is it really compatible with God's will for you?

Step III ... *Look Up:* "Jesus lifted up his eyes." He saw *above* the problem. On the human level, His senses told Him that this problem was hopeless. Lazarus was dead. But He "lifted up his eyes," He looked above His human consciousness to God. And on that level, there is only the perfect solution.

In this step, you turn away from the external condition. "Turn away when I'm in such emotional pain I could scream? You can't be serious!"

But we are. You have to detach yourself from the situation, enough so you can see it from a higher perspective. If you've been concentrating on the problem, you are part of the problem. To see it from a higher perspective is to begin to see it as God sees it. This shifts you over so that you become part of the solution.

Staying caught up in the problem renders you powerless to change it. A problem can never be solved by operating at the same level which created it in the first place. In fact, by staying at that level, your prayer becomes simply another form of worry, because you are constantly praying about it instead of letting go. And this amounts to actually affirming and validating the problem!

Step IV ... *Give Thanks:* Faced with a serious situation (and don't you agree that being dead for four days is serious?), Jesus gave thanks *before* Lazarus was resurrected. "Father, I thank thee." Can you imagine a more incredible show of gratitude and faith?

Make it a rule to let gratitude be part of your

103

prayers. That means giving thanks *before* your prayers are answered. It's easy to give thanks after you get your wish, but that's not a show of faith. It is just plain courtesy. Gratitude *before* your prayers are answered shows faith.

Also, giving thanks in advance indicates your belief in the power of prayer, sending a very subtle but essential message to your subconscious mind. This makes your prayer not a matter of asking but of knowing. It is not begging God for something you don't have, but thanking God for all the good which is already yours, whether here or on the way.

Step V ... *Speak the Word:* "He cried with a loud voice, 'Lazarus, come out.' " You call forth real soul power when you pray. Let yourself hear your prayer, whether it is silent or aloud. Really hear what you are saying. Don't worry about God's hearing it, "Your Father knows what you need before you ask him" (Mt. 6:8). Remember, you are not trying to inspire God. You are praying to inspire yourself. The phrase *"with a loud voice"* indicates that we're to speak the words (silently or audibly) with confidence.

Step VI ... *Release:* "Unbind him, and let him go." Jesus knew that once a prayer is completed, it is necessary to release it. God's perfect plan is being accomplished, and so we trust and let go. What farmer would plant his seeds, only to keep digging them up to see if they are growing? Neither should you, if you've faithfully followed the first five steps, keep checking for results. Release it. Just as God's rain, sun, and soil will bring forth the farmer's crop, so will God's love, peace, and strength bring forth your good.

CHECK OUT YOUR PRAYERS

These six steps of prayer are not, as we said, carved in stone. You may eventually discover others which are especially helpful to you, but this is a good place to begin. So, see if your prayers incorporate these six steps which Jesus used with such spectacular success.

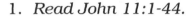

1. *Read John 11:1-44.*

2. How sure are you that what you want is what's best for you? Are you humble enough to get out of the way so that God's will can be revealed to you? Since God doesn't speak in a loud voice, start becoming aware of your feelings and intuitions. Keep on the lookout for signs. *Each evening before retiring, spend a few minutes reviewing the day for clues as to God's will. Write them down on your own paper.*

3. Be sure that you are doing your share to have your prayer answered. *Make a list of the steps you are taking to have your prayer answered.* For example, if your prayer is to find a better job, your list could include reading the "want ads" daily, going to school to retrain yourself, brushing up on your job skills, and staying centered in the assurance that God knows what's best for you. Whatever you are doing for yourself, write it down.

4. *Analyze your list and see what else you can do to work with God.* Are you looking at the problem, or are you looking to God as the solution? *What specific steps can you take to "look up" from the problem?* You may want to put a reminder on your bathroom mirror or a piece of tape on your watch so that every time you see it you remember that God is in charge.

Or you may opt for a little prayer that you can say throughout the day like: "God, I want to know You more. I want to serve You more. I want to love You more. I am willing to let You take charge of my life. Show me Your will and Your way, God. I am ready."

5. Can you be thankful that your good is on the way? If not, why not? *Write out a statement of thanksgiving now.*

6. *Before going any further, write out the six steps of Jesus' prayer.*

7. *Put aside time each day to pray.* Most people find that saying their prayers aloud is most effective, but however you say them, either out loud or silently, pray daily. And incorporate into your own prayers the six steps which Jesus used.

OFF THE MAIN TRAIL

 All people of the Earth have a connection to the Divine. Everyone has equal access to God. Create a universal prayer which you feel could be used by every person of this planet, regardless of culture, location, or religion.

STEPPING-STONE

 Actively and consciously appreciate the good things in your life.

Don't be satisfied with saying "Thank You, God, for my good." Actively inventory and appreciate a specific good in your life every day. "God, I am thankful for my children," or "God, I am thankful for my sense of humor," or "God, I am thankful for my friends." A good time to do this is in the morning on your way to work or at some other regular time.

God answers your prayers.

*Most of the evils in life arise from man's being
unable to sit still in a room.*
                                        —Blaise Pascal

There is only one way to experience "the silence"
and that is to be silent, physically and emotionally
silent. One of the best ways to accomplish this is
through the process called meditation.

SMALL INVESTMENTS BRING BIG BENEFITS

Sitting quietly, with the body relaxed and the
mind stilled, brings many physical and emotional
benefits. It reduces tension and stress, lightens anxiety, lowers blood pressure, increases energy levels,
improves sleep patterns, helps to decrease harmful
body chemicals and increase beneficial ones. It does
all this and much more.

Yet these physical, mental, and emotional benefits
cannot begin to compare with the greatest benefit, the
one we actually enter the silence for, and that is the

experience of knowing God and of activating our own divine qualities.

Since the within of us is so vast, it seems obvious that we should direct our attention to our inner core, dipping into the eternal wellspring of life which we find there. During these times of stillness, we want to let go of all reservations, all preconceived ideas, all personal willfulness, and then surrender completely to Spirit.

Meditation is not prayer. Put simply, prayer is talking to God whereas meditation is allowing God to talk to you. You do this by getting quiet and intentionally directing your attention to your inner self, to the secret place of the Most High.

SOUL-TALK

I listen to God.

1. _____

2. _____

3. _____

SOUL-THOUGHTS

MEDITATION—WHAT? WHEN? WHERE? HOW?

If you are in the habit of regularly spending time in the silence, your activity for this Adventure is to continue this vital practice. At the same time, be open to any new direction which may be revealed to you as a result of your being on *The Quest*. Also, read the balance of this adventure. Perhaps you will discover an idea that will heighten your experience.

WHAT?

Before determining what meditation is, let's see what it is not. Meditation is not:

—an altered state of consciousness

—a "high"

—an attempt to solve problems

—an escape from reality

—self-hypnosis

—prayer

We like this definition of meditation: the conscious direction of one's attention to the inner self. You begin by relaxing your body and then turning your mind inward to the stillness, resting in the beautiful sense of your oneness with God.

111

WHEN?

Regularity is the key to meaningful meditation. Try to meditate at the same time each day. However, avoid meditating when you are hungry (which can distract you) or immediately after meals (which can make you drowsy). Either of these is counterproductive to entering the silence.

Choose a time to meditate when you are most physically and emotionally comfortable. Allow enough time so that you are not pressured to terminate your meditation prematurely. End it because you are finished, not because you have an appointment nagging in the back of your mind.

WHERE?

The best place to meditate is the place you feel best! Where do you feel the most comfortable? Is it quiet? Is it practical to meditate there? If so, then you have found your place.

Regularity and consistency apply to location as well as time. Always try to meditate in the same place. If you can set aside a special room in your home to do your spiritual reading and meditation, this would be ideal. Just walking into the room would prepare you for the silence.

However, few of us have that luxury, and so the next best thing is to have a special chair in a special corner of a room to be used for your meditation times and spiritual work. This is perfectly acceptable and serves quite well, as long as you can surround yourself with quiet when you are in your chair.

Maybe you have a favorite outdoor spot, one which has a minimum of distractions and is easy to get

to. You will find the right place for your quiet times.
The main thing to keep in mind is that it should be as
free from activity and noise as possible.

HOW?

There are many meditation techniques taught and
practiced. If you are happy with your present one, by
all means stay with it. If you have never meditated or
are not completely satisfied with your present method,
the following suggestions might help you.

THE PREPARATION:

1. Approach your time of meditation with joy and
with a positive attitude. Have a gentle sense of expectancy, knowing that your good awaits you. Look forward to resting in the quiet world of God within you.

2. Be sure any clothing or jewelry is not restrict-
ing.

3. Sit in a comfortable chair. (It is not wise to lie
down as this is too much of a cue to sleep.)

THE EXPERIENCE:

Have you noticed how curious and active monkeys are? Yet give them something to occupy them
(like a large colored ball to hold) and their curiosity
about other things immediately wanes.

That's the way the mind works, but it is infinitely
more curious and more active than the most hyper-
energized monkey. Our mental activity and curiosity
are our most extraordinary assets in the pursuit of
knowledge. But it is also our most frustrating liability
in our pursuit of knowing God. Why? Because it's so
difficult for us to keep our minds quiet enough to listen!

One way to do this is to take a lesson from the monkeys and their large colored ball. In your meditation, find something on which to dwell. That "something" could be internally listening to a sound or a word or paying close attention to your breath. Some people feel comfortable with dwelling on the phrase *"I AM,"* internally saying *"I"* as they inhale and *"AM"* as they exhale. The silent phrase is then repeated continuously throughout the meditation time.

One good way to begin a meditation is by concentrating on your breathing. Just focus on your breath and follow it as you gently inhale and exhale. When you feel you are ready to turn your attention inward, take three slow deep breaths, each one deeper than the previous. These three deep breaths will eventually act as a signal, a cue to prepare you for your meditation. (We will be referring to them as "signal breaths.") After exhaling the last deep breath, switch your attention to your special phrase or word and resolutely follow it. As distractions impose themselves on your mind, gently bring your attention back to this point of focus which will act like a colored ball for your mind to hold onto as you merge with the stillness within.

Disregard all passing thoughts. Become indifferent to them. Of course, your mind will introduce, and attempt to entertain, all sorts of thoughts and feelings. Do not fight them. Just allow these thoughts and feelings to pass through. Keep on gently bringing back your attention to the process. Always be aware of the experience you are going through.

Expect Nothing: Don't be at all concerned with how you are doing. The more you are concerned, the less you are in the stillness. Meditation is not the time for concern about the challenges in your life. There is plenty of time later for that.

If your attention wanders, bring it back to the process of meditation. Don't battle with your mind. Don't try to get rid of thoughts. Nonresistance is the key to success. Your tranquil awareness and focus are really all that are needed.

When you are finished with your meditation, return gently to full awareness. Allow yourself to savor the experience.

A SHORT RECAP

1. Select a regular time for your meditation.

2. Sit upright in a comfortable chair and with comfortable clothing.

3. Begin by concentrating on your breathing. Then take your signal breaths. After the third breath, shift your attention to your special phrase, such as "I AM."

4. Empty your mind of all thoughts except your special words. As thoughts enter your mind, merely observe them and allow them to pass through. Be nonresistant.

5. When finished, take time to savor the experience.

DON'T BE DISCOURAGED

If you meditate for the first time and are harassed by thoughts, feelings, and especially memories, don't despair. In attempting to tame the mind to listen, you may have to go through some retraining in the beginning. But if you keep your attention on your "colored ball," you will soon see that the mind will quiet down and you will eventually experience that still, small voice within you.

1. *Take at least twenty minutes each day to spend some time in the stillness.* You can do this by meditating or by any other process you may have discovered for yourself. (This time in the stillness is so important that this activity should be adopted as a lifetime habit.)

2. *One of the strengths of a* Quest *group is being able to select one person to lead the others in a meditation session. This person can slowly read the steps given above, allowing several minutes of silence. This time of silence can be increased as the group grows more familiar with the process.*

OFF THE MAIN TRAIL

Plan to set aside one full day this week (or as soon as possible) for silence. You will be doing what Jesus would sometimes invite His disciples to do after an intense period of ministering: "Come away by yourselves to a lonely place, and rest a while" (Mk. 6:31), and they would depart for a quiet place.

A day in silence will inspire, motivate, and regenerate you. So turn off the radio, television, stereo, and telephone. Relax. Spend as much time as you can in the stillness, being open to whatever thoughts and feelings wander in. Don't try to control them. But do try to keep them as much as possible on love, beauty, peace, joy, and all things positive.

This venture should be done alone. Or it can be done in the company of one or two other people who will share the space and silence with you. In the latter case, the rules must be set and agreed upon before starting.

It's a good idea to keep a notebook handy so that

you can record all of the insights and feelings and ideas which you will receive.

STEPPING-STONE

 When unexpectedly delayed, for instance in traffic or checkout lines, consciously take time to relax.

You have a choice when unexpected delays interrupt your life. If you allow habit to rule, you may automatically become annoyed at the interruption in your schedule and feel stressed. But if you *consciously* consider your options, you can decide to use the time as an opportunity for growth. The trick is to be aware, to make the decision for yourself and not let events dictate what your reaction will be.

While on this Adventure, use any delay as an opportunity to reconnect with that haven of peace within you. Take your three "signal breaths," cuing yourself to relax and lift your emotions and thoughts to higher ground. You might even want to hear the words "Peace, be still" echoing in your mind.

By doing this *Stepping-Stone,* you will have turned a stress-filled situation into a restorative, spirit-filled one. You will have exchanged negative energy for positive energy.

You listen to God.

Bibliography:
Beyond the Relaxation Response, Herbert Benson, M.D., Times Books, New York, 1984.
An Easy Guide to Meditation, Roy Eugene Davis, CSA Press, Lakemont, Georgia, 1978.

GOD'S WILL

*The Lord God is subtle, but malicious
he is not.*

—Albert Einstein

A botanist was collecting flower samples along the edge of a cliff. Stretching for a rare flower, he lost his footing and began falling toward the breaking surf hundreds of feet below. Wildly reaching for a small tree jutting out from the side, he barely managed to grab it. Hanging tenuously by one hand, he couldn't see the narrow pathway carved into the side of the cliff a few feet below his dangling legs. He called for help, but no one was near.

Soon he felt his hand slipping as his grip began to weaken. A sickening fear overtook him. In desperation he cried out, "God, help me. What shall I do?" The sky opened with flashes of lightening and a voice thundered, "Let go of the tree!"

The botanist couldn't believe his ears! Was this God speaking to him, telling him to let go of the only *thing saving him from the angry water below? He called out again, "God help me." Again the voice boomed, "Let go of the tree!"*

The man, by now desperately fatigued, groaned, "Are You God?"

The voice answered, "Yes."

The man, hearing the pounding surf below, looked up to the sky and timidly asked, "Is anybody else up there?"

How many times in our lives have we not wanted to accept God's will? How many times do we find ourselves still dangling, because we're not willing to trust God enough?

But, simply put, God's will is the unrelenting desire in you to express your divine potential. More simply put? God's will is radiant health, abundant prosperity, limitless love, eternal happiness, and the knowledge that you are part of God. Most simply put? God's will is God, seeking to express in you and as you.

SOUL-TALK

 God's will is my will.

1. _____

2. _____

3. _____

SOUL-THOUGHTS

Note: Just a reminder to tell you to be sure you are thorough in writing your *Soul-Thoughts*. Keep in mind that these observations are your log for your journey. They chronicle your discoveries about yourself. Be as honest and accurate in writing about your feelings and impressions as you possibly can.

GET IT RIGHT THE FIRST TIME

When faced with a problem we can't resolve, it's natural to ask others what to do. We gather and categorize their advice and, armed with all of this input, we attempt to change our lives. And, to some extent, we do change them. After all, our lives are like modeling clay. We can give them any form we want.

But clay is lifeless. It stays in one shape as the world around it changes. So we find we are constantly remolding ourselves in an attempt to keep up with the changes all about us. Molding and remolding each of the endlessly variable aspects of our lives becomes a full-time job. A never-ending job. It leaves us exhausted. But even worse than any of that, we never get it just ... quite ... right!

WHAT IS GOD'S WILL, ANYWAY?

Let's do some activities now to help clarify the concept of God's will. We want to take "God's will" out of its lofty-sounding, theoretical plane and bring it down to earth so that we can get some direction.

1. *Did you ever do something, knowing that it was not God's will, but did it anyway? Describe it.* Perhaps it involved a relationship, a job, a purchase, and so on. Maybe you accepted a date with someone you didn't trust. Maybe you filed an insurance claim that you knew was dishonest.

2. *Have you ever made a decision which you felt was God's will? What was it that gave you that feeling? Describe that decision and your feelings now.*

3. *What was the outcome of that decision? Did it turn out to be God's will? How do you know?* (When it's God's will, everyone eventually wins, remember?) *Answer this in detail now.*

4. *If there's a decision you are having trouble making right now, what can you do that you have not done in the past to know what God's will is?* It might be something like sitting quietly on the edge of your bed every morning before you begin your day and asking God for *explicit* guidance. Whatever it is, be sure it's something different from what you've done in the past.

5. *Carefully listen and observe throughout the day for God's will.* Sounds like an easy activity, doesn't it? Yet it's too easy to walk through life like a robot, endlessly repeating our daily tasks, oblivious to any direction other than yesterday's routine. If this is happening to you, obviously you'll want to change it. How? Observe, observe, observe!

Important: God doesn't speak in a loud voice. With open eyes so you can see, open ears so you can

hear, and an open heart so you can feel, you will have
your answer.

OFF THE MAIN TRAIL

*In several paragraphs, write out what you believe
is God's will for the future of the human race. What is
the end goal?*

STEPPING-STONE

Encourage someone you know to talk about himself or herself. Be genuinely interested in what this person has to say.

True listening is the most personal form of giving. It's an opportunity to give of yourself to someone else. True listening is a transference of love between two people. So be sure you are listening with your heart.

Spend some time each day this week listening, *really* listening, to someone else.

You are open to God's will.

GOD FIRST

When down in the mouth, remember Jonah:
he came out all right.

—Thomas Edison

Assuming you want to put God first in your life, how do you go about doing that? In theory it sounds great, but how do you put it into practice?

That's the challenge of this teaching, and there is no easy answer. There is no magic mechanism that automatically places God first in your life, but that doesn't mean it can't be done. There is a way you can do it, and that is to be on the lookout for occasions when your thoughts and actions are not reflecting your best self. As soon as you can identify this, you can bring them back on course.

Like so many meaningful changes, this is simple. But that doesn't mean it's easy. We are so accustomed to thinking and doing things in the same old (and often destructive) way that to shift them from "me first" to "God first" just doesn't feel natural. So we may end up rationalizing our dislike for a neighbor by saying no one else likes him either, or we may justify our less-than-honest answers on our income tax forms by saying everybody does it.

Still, seeking first the kingdom of God is not really that difficult if we're willing to start monitoring ourselves. The teaching which Jesus has for us here is that we seek the kingdom of God by looking inside ourselves. Staying in close touch with the kingdom within results in the freedom to live life in an easy manner because all of the details are being handled for us by God.

God first, and then all else "comes with the territory." By keeping God first, we have the pleasure, the joy, of observing every situation resolving itself in a new and wonderful way.

Speaking of joy, this is probably a good time to bring up the fact that putting God first does not in any way mean we must live lives of pious solemnity. It doesn't mean that we can't have fun, plenty of laughs, and lighthearted attitudes. Quite the contrary. You will find, if anything, that when you put God first, your life automatically becomes easier and happier because there is less stress and worry. Things are working out in the best possible way and with the least amount of effort.

SOUL-TALK

I put God first.

1. _____

2. _____

3. _____

_____

SERVING TRUTH

This chapter gives us our first indication as to just what a disparity there is between the understanding of something and the putting of that something into practice. A few years back it was chic to "find Truth." People went to the mountains to sit in contemplation, they traveled to holy men to be taught and disciplined, they fasted and prayed and denied their bodies, seeking insight into Truth.

But finding Truth is really the easy part, as we said in an earlier teaching, it is *serving* Truth that is the challenge. Each of us probably knows enough

Truth right now to keep us busy for a lifetime. The question we have to answer is "Am I *serving* the Truth that I already know?" If we have not placed God first in all areas of our lives, we are not serving Truth and there is little joy that comes to us.

1. You have identified certain challenges you are facing as you journey on your quest. *In retrospect, were there any challenges in the past which you solved by putting God first? Describe one or two of these.* (Perhaps you put God first out of frustration because the problem seemed too overwhelming, and God was all that was left to turn to.)

If there was never a time you actually put God first, then describe the time you came the closest to doing so.

2. *What's going on in your life right now that you feel can be improved by putting God first?*

Exactly how are you going to put God first?

3. Can you think of an example from your life or anyone else's life when putting God first, seeking first the kingdom, resulted in unexpected good? Write out the details. If you don't have a real life example, how about an example from a book or movie?

OFF THE MAIN TRAIL

Do you entirely agree with this statement: "*All we have to do is put God first in our lives. When we do this, everything that we need to make us happy will be provided for us*"?

If so, write a few paragraphs on why it is true for you.

If not, how would you amend the statement?

After you have amended it, write a few paragraphs explaining your changes.

STEPPING-STONE

Read some inspirational literature every day.

For at least 15 minutes each day, read inspirational books or magazines (something in addition to *The Quest*). Keep your mind open to being nourished with new concepts, fresh insights, and positive ideas.

You put God first.

*P*ERSONAL POWERLESSNESS

It isn't easy being green.
—Kermit the Frog

"I admit *personal* powerlessness to improve my life." Is that difficult for you to say?

If it is, can you apply the statement to some persistent challenge in your life (perhaps the one that prompted you to begin *The Quest*) and feel any better about saying it? "I admit *personal* powerlessness over whether my company will be closing the plant." That's straightforward enough. But what about, "I admit *personal* powerlessness over my husband's smoking," or "I admit *personal* powerlessness over the poor relationship with my wife," or "I admit *personal* powerlessness to heal my body"? We tend to balk at such admissions because we want to feel we can affect our own lives. We want to feel in control.

Yet how can we ever be in complete control of our lives? There are too many variables: the economy, the weather, political decisions, the health of our loved ones, our jobs, and an endless procession of events. So, in a very real sense, we are *personally* powerless. We can do some superficial tinkering and make some short-term improvements—a vacation, a new job, a new husband or wife, an operation, a new car or stereo, but changes cannot make us permanently happy if they begin and end with the human "us."

It is only when changes are initiated and implemented from our spiritual selves that our powerlessness changes to power. That's because such changes are anchored in God's will for us which, of course, is absolute good. We will be happy only to the extent that we ally our human power, our human resources, with God-power. (But that's the next Teaching.)

Meanwhile, if you've been stumbling over any of those tormenting needs to control, they really have to be cleared from the path before you can proceed on your journey. Some of them are terribly heavy and require a lot of muscle power to be moved aside. Yet by doing this, you'll be opening the way for the arrival of true power.

SOUL-TALK

 God is my help.

1. _____

2. _____

3. _____

FROM "BATTERY-POWERED" TO GOD-POWERED

The only resource a battery-powered instrument has, its only power, is in its batteries. Yet no matter how much the batteries are charged, as long as they are separated from their power source, they will eventually become ineffective.

You have only a limited amount of *human* power. And no matter how much you have been given, as long as you are separated from your Power Source, you will eventually become ineffective. But when you operate from your spiritual core, you are plugged into the infinite Source of good, a Source that never loses Its power.

Any changes created and sustained solely by your

"battery-powered" human self must eventually run down. When you rely exclusively on yourself, you have only your human energy, intelligence, and resources to nurture such changes. But when changes come from your spiritual self, that part of you "connected" to God, then you share in God's power. And that never wears out.

Jesus stayed "plugged in." With such power at His command, He succeeded in elevating His human self until it fused with His divine self. We on "the Quest" are also working at upgrading our human selves. It is a continual process, one which starts with the recognition that, at this stage of our development, we are personally powerless to improve our lives. We can't do it alone. We need God.

1. *Name three things you thought you could control which you have found out you couldn't.* An example could be your first child. Remember all the plans you had? Or your venture into the stock market.

a. _____

b. _____

c. _____

2. *Name three situations in your life when your admission of personal helplessness brought about the solution to a problem.* For example, the TV wouldn't work so you took it to a repair shop.

a. _____

b. _____

c. _____

3. *Are there any things in your life right now over which you should admit personal helplessness? Hint:* If they have been in your life longer than you wanted them, chances are you can't control them. *List all of them.*

4. *Write the following statement for each of them:*
"*I admit personal powerlessness over_____ .*"

5. Comment on your feelings as you wrote out your admissions of powerlessness.

OFF THE MAIN TRAIL

Why is the word personal *such a key word in the phrase "I admit* personal *powerlessness to improve my life"? Is there a difference between the "personal" you and another part of you? Explain.*

Actively and consciously let *things happen, rather than trying to* make *them happen.*

This week, "go with the flow." Don't try to force anything into or out of your life, whether it is at home or at work. Allow yourself to be in the current of life without swimming against the current. Of course there will be things that need your attention, that you will have to make decisions about. But, more than ever before in your life, try to experience what it is like to let things happen without your forcing them in the direction you think they should go. This week relax, release, and let go.

God is your help.

*S*URRENDER 16

"Your Majesty, I have bad news and good news."
"What is the bad news?"
*"Our fortress is in shambles, we are out of ammunition,
and half the men have deserted. We will never be able
to defend ourselves against the barbarians."*
*"That's terrible news. How could there be any good
news?"*
"There are no barbarians!"

It was a battlefield, and the crabs were losing! We
had never seen anything like it. Crabs were squashed,
smashed, and strewn about the highway as if hurled
down from the heavens. The whole mess came about
because armies of large land crabs were heading east,
crossing the shore road on their way to the beach.

If one drove carefully, it was relatively easy to
drive around them or straddle them with the wheels of
a car. They didn't travel all that quickly and, since
they were built so low to the ground, vehicles could
easily pass over them.

The problem was that as a car approached them,
the crabs would see it coming and raise themselves up
as high as they could, waving their giant front claws
threateningly over their heads.

These were not small crabs! Raised up with their

claws above their heads, they stood over twelve inches high which, unfortunately for them, was high enough to touch the bottoms of the speeding cars!

It was this foolhardy show of bravado which proved to be their downfall. As long as the crabs moved normally and kept their natural height, one could drive around or over them. But when they felt challenged, they became aggressive, assumed an attack posture and, of course, were themselves "attacked."

Now, with all that crab meat on the road, the birds flocked in. It seemed as if every sea gull in Florida were dining on *crabs à la roadside* that day. It was a royal feast.

But the reaction of the gulls toward the cars was much different than that of the crabs. When the gulls were approached by cars, they didn't challenge the cars, they didn't get upset at having their meals interrupted, they didn't flap their wings in anger. They merely flew away! There was a total surrender on their part, an absolute nonresistance, a total willingness to let "the enemy" pass by without as much as a second look. After the cars passed by, they simply resumed their gourmet meals.

Crabs and gulls were both confronted by the same serious problem—speeding cars. One fought with the problem and lost. The other surrendered to it and won.

We've been admonished by Jesus to "resist not evil" (Mt. 5:39 KJV), but how do we react when faced with a problem which we feel is "hundreds of times our size"? Like the crabs, do we want to "do battle" with it? Do we want to sharpen our weapons and slay it? Do we want to fight with it and subdue it on *our* terms?

Or are we more like the sea gulls? Are we content to recognize that we have other than tools of battle available to us?

Like the sea gulls, we have been given the ability to "rise above" our troubles, to see them from a different perspective: a higher one. When we are willing to stop struggling and simply surrender, the Spirit of God lifts us aloft. We find ourselves walking the high road, where our burden is easy and our yoke is light.

SOUL-TALK

I surrender to God.

1. _____

2. _____

3. _____

SOUL-THOUGHTS

LIKE CLIMBING A LADDER

Can you climb to a higher rung on a ladder if you don't let go of the lower rung? Neither can you climb to your good until you first let go of your difficulties. Letting go is surrendering.

However, surrendering is not quitting. That's an important distinction. To "let go and let God" means simply to "let go" of your doubts and fears of the outcome. It means to focus your attention *away from* the problem. Then, after letting go, you "let God" unfold the perfect plan for you.

A friend was laid off at a local airplane plant. Although he hated his job, he liked the security it had given him. Extremely worried, he tried his best to get back to work with the company, but after three months of unemployment he finally surrendered the problem to God. He kept actively looking for work but was so sure of getting the "perfect job" that he was able to release his anxiety. He "let go and let God."

Our friend did find a job, "The perfect job for me," he says. He works with his brother-in-law building custom boats in New England. He loves it. Working with his hands is something he had always wanted to do. He's making less money, but is happier than he ever was.

1. *In Adventure 15, you wrote a list of things over which you admitted powerlessness. Using the same list, write the following sentence:*

"*I surrender _____ to God.*"

For example, "I surrender my husband's smoking habit to God."

a. _____

b. _____

c. _____

2. *What were your thoughts while you were writing these statements? How did it feel to surrender these things? Do you now feel vulnerable? Write a few paragraphs on your feelings.*

TRANSFORMATIONAL SURRENDER

If you stay caught up in a problem, you can only grow to the height of the problem. There can be no other movement toward growth. It is a static situation, one of no change.

If you can truly turn the outcome of any situation over to God, this is transformational surrender. The decision itself begins the journey toward the solution.

With such reliance on God to supply the answer, your life is automatically transformed for the better. This is because in a transformational surrender, you are not only saying that God *has* the answer, you are saying that God *is* the answer.

OFF THE MAIN TRAIL

I am the place where God shines through,
  For He and I are one, not two,
He wants me where and how I am,
  I need not fear, nor will, nor plan.
If I just be relaxed and free,
  He'll carry out His plan through me.
                    —Anonymous

Comment on your interpretation of this poem.

Tell a different person a joke every day.

The wonderful thing about your telling a joke is that you laugh every time you tell it!

Laughter, joy, and cheerfulness will become a more constant part of your life as you journey ahead on *The Quest.* (Maybe you're noticing this already.) Laughter is good for us humans. It lifts our spirits, eases tension, and strengthens our physical bodies.

Telling someone a joke every day will remind you that life is to be lived joyously and that when we are truly centered in God, laughter and joy and peace are our constant companions.

You surrender to God.

*I*NNER CHANGE

"You'll never get me up in one of those things."
—A caterpillar, on seeing his first butterfly

One of the biggest frustrations in transforming your life is waiting for the outer circumstances to catch up with the new inner changes.

"I've been on *The Quest* for about four months now. When am I going to start seeing some meaningful changes in my life?" You may be tempted to go back to the old ways of thinking and acting because the circumstances in your life are not changing fast enough for you.

The truth is that if you have been working on *The Quest*, there *have* been changes—inner changes. You may not have detected them yet, but they are there and your life is already changing as a result of them. And it will keep on changing. Just because you are not aware of these changes doesn't mean they don't exist.

NEW PLATEAUS

Athletes deal with this when they train. They exercise to increase their stamina, but they've learned they can't detect these increases on a daily basis. It's almost as if their gains have to accumulate to a point where they can suddenly break through on a new plateau. Up until then, it had seemed as if no progress were being made. Now all at once it's extremely easy to run the distance which was such a struggle only a few days before. It's as if the heart and lungs finally say, "Okay, you win. I'll change. I'll be more efficient from now on."

Having reached this new plateau, the athlete continues to train. He continues his quest for more conditioning, aware as he trains that changes are taking place and that all he has to do is continue doing what he is doing and trusting the process.

SOUL-TALK

I am changing.

1. _____

2. _____

3. _____

SOUL-THOUGHTS

1. *The box at the beginning of Teaching 17 states that inner change is your greatest assignment in this lifetime. Do you agree? Why?*

If you don't agree, what do you feel is your greatest assignment?

2. *Give an example from your life where you tried to put "new wine" into an "old wineskin."* For example, you may have changed relationships, thinking it would make you happier.

3. *Do you sense an inner change in your life at this time? Describe how that inner change is affecting some of the circumstances of your life.*

If you don't sense an inner change, why do you feel that this is so, given the fact that you've been working on The Quest *for about four months?*

OFF THE MAIN TRAIL

Explain the statement in the Guidebook: "We can move away from our present circumstances, but if our consciousness hasn't changed, we will inevitably re-create the same circumstances because our consciousness will have supplied the only blueprint it knows." (Teaching 4, "What Am I?" may help you to answer this.)

STEPPING-STONE

Change something in your daily morning routine.

Remember that the purpose of these *Stepping-Stones* is to bring about larger changes. A change in your morning routine will set you up for other, more meaningful changes throughout the day. It will be a subtle reminder that your life will never be the same, that change is on the way.

The morning changes don't have to be big changes. For example, if you normally brush your teeth before you shower, brush them afterwards. If you normally read the editorial section of the paper first, read it last. Listen to a different radio station or watch a different television morning show. The assignment is simply to make some change in your morning routine while you are on Adventure 17.

—————————

You are changing.

*We have in the operation of our own minds
an illustration of how Divine Mind works.*
—Charles Fillmore

Just as a waterwheel generates maximum power when it *allows* the water to flow through it and turn it, so we generate the most power in our lives when we allow ideas from God-Mind to flow through our minds.

God can work in us only in this way. In fact, the most seemingly impossible conditions are resolved in a positive way when we let God-Mind work through our minds.

SOUL-TALK

My mind is one with God-Mind.

1. _____

2. _____

3. _____

SOUL-THOUGHTS

BRIGHT IDEAS

We can compare our thought process with the
process of God-Mind. Note we said thought *process*,
not thoughts. If our thoughts were always God-
thoughts, we would never experience anything but
perfect contentment. The fact that we may not, means
that there is a breakdown in communication between
God-Mind and our mind.

Cartoonists depict innovative ideas of their comic
strip characters by showing light bulbs turning on
above their heads. It's an apt analogy. We've all felt
the "light" go on at times. Perhaps there have been
times when you've also felt the "light of God" through
your mind too. These are the instances when you've
allowed God-Mind to flow through your mind.

1. *List the instances in your life when you feel that you were open and receptive to God's will and allowed God-Mind to flow through your mind and inspire you. (Look for the times in your life when you absolutely knew that the decision you had made was the right one.)*

2. This God-Mind Meditation is the only other activity for this Adventure. Rather than an activity which involves reading and writing, this activity is passive and needs only an acceptance.

God-Mind Meditation

Experience God-Mind as it flows through you by becoming quiet and still and centered. Before beginning, take some time to quiet your mind and your body.

Begin your God-Mind Meditation by speaking the phrase "God-Mind" aloud as you exhale. On the next exhale speak aloud, "my mind." Alternate these phrases with energy. Allow the relationship between the two to become evident, "God-Mind, my mind."

Ever so slowly, begin saying these phrases, "God-Mind, my mind," more and more quietly until they become a mere whisper. Repeat them as a whisper for a while until it feels right to internalize the phrases. Now, with the phrases inside of you, silently affirm "God-Mind" as you inhale while you continue to affirm "my mind" as you exhale. You are now breathing in "God-Mind" and breathing out "my mind."

Continue in this manner until you feel ready to end your God-Mind Meditation. Then take a few minutes to sit quietly and allow the process to complete itself.

Summary of God-Mind Meditation

1. Become quiet and still.

2. Begin saying aloud on alternate exhalations: "God-Mind," then "my mind."

3. Say these phrases more and more softly until you finally internalize them.

4. When internalized, silently say "God-Mind" when you inhale and "my mind" when you exhale.

5. Inhale "God-Mind," exhale "my mind."

6. Continue until it feels right to end.

OFF THE MAIN TRAIL

Many feel that The Gospel According to John is the most mystical of the four Gospels. The beginning of this beautiful gospel shows a progression of mind, idea, and expression. Read John 1:1-17 and write your thoughts on this progression.

Hint: Verses 1 through 3 deal with mind. Verses 4 through 13 deal with idea. Verses 13 through 17 deal with expression.

Silently send a loving thought to all people who call you on the phone.

This includes operators, salespeople, and friends. Before you pick up the phone, let it ring one extra time while you silently send love to the caller, even if you don't know who it is. Once you do know who it is, send another loving thought. When the person hangs up, take five seconds or so to send him or her a loving thought one more time. Do this all week.

Your mind is one with God-Mind.

LAW OF MIND ACTION

You never can tell what your thoughts will do
  In bringing you hate or love,
For thoughts are things, and their airy wings
  Are swifter than carrier doves.
They follow the law of the universe—
  Each thing must create its kind,
And they speed o'er the track to bring you back
  Whatever went out from your mind.
                    —Ella Wheeler Wilcox

When the British tennis star Gem Gilbert was a little girl, she watched in horror as her mother died of shock in the dentist chair during a tooth extraction. The experience had such a profoundly negative impact on her that for the next thirty years she refused to go to a dentist. Finally, she was suffering from a toothache of such severity that she agreed to have a dentist come to her home to see if he could help her. He arrived to find her surrounded by her family, her friends, her personal physician, and even her minister. Upon examining the tooth, the dentist informed Gem that he would have to extract it. But before he could even begin, she died!

After a lengthy obituary detailing her life and athletic accomplishments, the article in the *London Daily Mail* concluded that she was killed by thirty years of thought!

Apple seeds can only grow apple trees. Dogs can only produce puppies. Continually give builders the same blueprint and they will continually build the same house. Regardless of location, time of year, or builder, a blueprint for a white stucco house with a white picket fence will yield a white stucco house with a white picket fence. How can it not? "But I wanted a red brick house without a fence." Well, then create a different blueprint.

It's been estimated that we have 60,000 separate thoughts each day. That's about fifty thoughts each minute! How astounding. It shows that we have an incredible ability to process ideas. Yet what's even more astounding is the fact that about 99 percent of today's thoughts are the same as yesterday's! No wonder it is so difficult for us to change our lives.

How can our lives be anything different than our thoughts? God's desire for us is absolute good. It is our minds that decide what part of God's good will becomes part of our lives. You can see that the choice has to be ours, otherwise the concept of free will is a hoax.

If what happens in our lives is the result of anything other than *our* thinking, then it is not *we* who decide our fates. It would be believing that God gives us free will but then capriciously takes it back by interfering in our choices.

Happily, that is not so. God works *with* us to bring into our lives whatever *we* desire and expect. In God-Mind, there is perfect good for us. God is the

Master Builder, but we have provided the blueprint.

SOUL-TALK

 I change my thoughts, I change my world.

1. _____

2. _____

3. _____

SOUL-THOUGHTS

POWER IN A SMALL PACKAGE

It may be difficult to accept the fact that thoughts have any power. After all, what is a thought but a few millionths of a watt of electricity generated in a computer made of flesh, undetectable by all but the most sensitive equipment. How can something so minuscule change our lives which are so complex?

It may even be tempting to think that a thought is not a real thing, but there is no doubt that it is. If it were not, a thought of fear could not increase adrenalin and cholesterol, dilate your blood vessels, and create the many other physical changes in your body. If a thought were not a real thing, then a thought of love could not strengthen the immune system and infuse the body with other beneficial chemicals. Yes, thoughts are things. Thoughts are energy.

Years ago Albert Einstein said that energy and matter are related and that neither is created nor destroyed. Rather, he said, energy is changed into matter and matter into energy.

Since thoughts are energy, our thoughts must affect us. There is no way that they cannot, any more than the energy of a fire cannot affect a piece of coal. Our "thought" energy is transmuted into the "matter," the circumstances, of our lives.

Do you still want your life to change? Then you will have to change the blueprint, because the universe is plastic to your thoughts and desires. The entire universe is waiting for you to tell it what to do. Your thoughts are the blueprint from which it works.

1. *Think of your earliest thought about a life-changing experience.* Perhaps it was a decision to marry someone or to get a divorce. Maybe it was a decision to change jobs or to have a child. *Describe how that thought led to your eventual action. Be as detailed as you can.*

2. *Are you facing a decision now? Write down your thoughts about it.*

3. *Will these thoughts lead you where you want to go? Explain how they will or will not.*

GATEKEEPER REVISITED

Remember the gatekeeper—your ability to filter out thoughts presented to you? Throughout the day you are constantly bombarded with the thoughts of others. The most insidious of these are the commercials on television and advertisements on billboards and in newspapers and magazines. They are messages that attempt to direct your thinking.

4. *What commercials or advertisements do you disagree with? Name three and list the reasons you disagree with them.*

For example, maybe you don't like being told that you must smoke a cigarette or drink a certain beverage to be sophisticated.

5. *What popular thinking do you agree or disagree with and why?*

Perhaps you agree with popular thought about economic good times or bad times. You may agree or disagree with the implication of the news media that we live in a dangerous world.

CHANGING THE FRAMEWORK

     A sculptor who works in clay will first make a metal framework that reflects the general shape of the work he or she has in mind. Clay is then added to this shape to round it out and give it details. In just such a manner, our lives reflect the framework of our dominant thoughts about ourselves. Our day-to-day choices are the "clay" that fills in all of the details.

     6. *Think about your life. What do you feel is the framework around which you fill in the details? What is your dominant thought about yourself? Write it out.*

Paying attention to the words you use is an excellent way to discover what your thinking is. After all, words are just thoughts converted into sound. The words you use with strong emphasis tend to form the experiences of your life. Do you say things like this?

"I'm such a mess."

"I just can't save money."

"My relationships always end up as a disaster."

"I'm terrible at spelling."

"I always get lost."

"If there's a cold around, I'll catch it."

Another good test is to ask yourself what opinions that others have about you are you accepting as your own?

"You're a real scatterbrain."

"You're so stupid."

"Poor thing, you've always been so sickly."

 7. The purpose of this Teaching is to get you thinking about your thinking. *What major shift in your thinking is needed at this point in your life? Be specific in your details.*

Select two people who are strong examples of the law of mind action. Your choices will be people whose powerful ideas were infused with passionate emotions, creating a single-visioned drive toward success. (Their ideas of success might not be yours, but the law of mind action worked to produce what they wanted.) The people can be historical figures or fictional characters from books or movies. Describe how the lives and events of these two figures were a direct result of the actions of their minds. Identify the ideas and emotions which they employed to bring about the results.

STEPPING-STONE

Set the framework for your day.

Decide each morning just what kind of attitude you will bring into the day. Make a decision to set the framework for your day. Here are some suggestions:

Today I keep it simple.

Today I give everything the light touch.

Today I keep it humorous.

Today I am understanding.

Today I am loving.

Today I accept.

Today I am patient.

You change your thoughts, you change your world.

THE POWER OF THE SPOKEN WORD

"Death and life are in the power of the tongue."
—Proverbs 18:21

We are able to read each other's minds by listening to each other's words! That is how we can communicate our needs and desires to one another. Carefully listening to someone will tell you what he or she is all about.

More importantly, you can read your own mind, ascertain your own consciousness, by listening to your own words. Your fears, your worries, your desires, your likes, and your loves are all expressed throughout your speech, in what you say. If you carefully listen to yourself, you will know what you are about.

Since your words mirror your thoughts, it logically follows that as you change your thoughts, your words will automatically change. Yet illogical as it seems, you don't have to wait for a change of consciousness to change your words. You can change them any time you want to, and in fact, consciously changing your words will eventually change your thinking! You can, so to speak, "fake it until you make it."

Because the brain doesn't know the difference between something real and something vividly imagined, you can talk yourself into a change of thinking! When you speak the word, you send a signal down a neural pathway. In a sense, you "cut a groove" in the brain. The more you use this pathway, the more pronounced the "groove" gets, and the more easily your thinking automatically follows the groove. So, to constantly declare, "I *can* have a loving relationship with my daughter-in-law," in the face of past and present evidence to the contrary, will change your thinking. Before long you will believe that it can be done. Thus convinced, your every word will mirror this change of consciousness, and your actions will follow.

SOUL-TALK

 I speak only positive words.

1. _____

2. _____

3. _____

SOUL-THOUGHTS

HOW COHERENT ARE YOU?

Remember the example of laser light. It is light that is in phase; it is "coherent" light. It gets all of its power from its unity of purpose.

Now apply that principle to your words. Are your words in phase? Are they "coherent"? Are you consistent in proclaiming your good, or are you sending mixed messages to yourself and to the universe? Is there a unity of purpose in your words?

1. *Take a word inventory. Each night before you go to bed, take stock of the words you used throughout the day. Write down every word that you used that could have been better chosen. Write what you said and what you could have said that would have better reflected your good.* (You will need to use your own paper, possibly a personal journal, throughout this Adventure.)

For example: I said, "I'll never get over this cold." I could have said, "I'm going to feel better tomorrow."

I said, "I'll never find anyone to share my life with." I could have said, "I'm attracting the perfect mate now."

2. *What words of others did you accept as your own today? Make a list in your separate notebook.* If you accepted their words about you as true, then their words have become your words. (This is true for the positive words you accept as well as the negative ones. That's why it's always good to spend as much time as possible with positive people who are not afraid to give someone a compliment.)

Example: I believed Joe when he said, "You'll never sell your home during this recession."

How can you change those words to reflect what you want in your life?

Example: "Others have sold their homes, I will too."

3. *Without being critical or judgmental, listen carefully and analyze the words of others. Listen for key phrases, especially those which you feel they are using to limit themselves. Each day write a paragraph on one person's words that had the greatest impact on you that day.* (Again you will write in your separate notebook or journal.)

4. *If you are working with a Quest group, at each meeting agree on a statement to affirm. Speak this statement as a group with excitement and expectancy. Do this for the remainder of The Quest.* (You may want to use the same statement at every meeting, or you may feel it more meaningful to change statements each meeting.)

5. *Use the power of your spoken word at least once each day to affirm the truth to someone.*

169

Examples of this might be:

"You look so healthy."

"I know things will work out well for you."

"You have the strength to handle this."

"God is in charge of your life."

OFF THE MAIN TRAIL

 For one full day this week, speak only positive, life-filled words. If you slip and say something that you don't feel reflects you at your Christ essence, begin again.

This assignment may be more difficult than it looks. This is because our society spends a lot of time hashing over negative events. A quick review of the day's news brings home the fact that negativity is news. Even the most cursory listening shows that people love to talk "gloom and doom." Drenched in such negativity, we can easily start believing that such pessimistic thinking and speaking are normal.

STEPPING-STONE

 Start each morning by singing a positive song.

As soon as you wake up in the morning, start singing or humming or whistling a song. Don't wait until you have taken a shower or had your breakfast. As soon as your eyes open and you are aware that you are awake, begin singing.

It's probably a good idea to put a memo in a conspicuous place to remind you. A song is usually not a top priority first thing in the morning, and so it's easy to forget to do it.

If your living arrangements are not conducive to

loud singing in the morning, you can always hum softly until you get a chance to really belt one out!

You speak only positive words.

Hitch your wagon to a star.
    —Ralph Waldo Emerson

"Excuse me, sir. Can you tell me how I can get to Carnegie Hall?"

"Practice, practice, practice!"

Our apologies! An old joke, but it fits so well that we couldn't resist. Practice, practice, practice! Practicing the correct use of your I AM is one of the surest ways to succeed in changing your life for the better.

It's so easy to misuse the I AM ("I am feeling rotten today," or "I am such a scatterbrain," or "I am sorry"), that it takes continual awareness and practice to change the habit. Try to estimate how many times a day you follow the words *I am* with something positive. Could be that it's not very often.

We're not suggesting that you start bragging about yourself, but there's nothing wrong with making some appropriate positive changes. Why not convert "I am feeling rotten" to "I am feeling great," or at least to "I am feeling better"? Why repeatedly use your I AM power to affirm *I am such a scatterbrain* when you can affirm *I am in charge* or, perhaps, *I am getting it together*? And why say "I am sorry" when a more accurate statement is "I apologize"? These are simple changes, but they serve to clear the debris from the path on which you are journeying. It's just a matter of practice, practice, practice.

SOUL TALK

I am loved.

1. _____

2. _____

3. _____

SOUL-THOUGHTS

BREAKING HABITS BY MAKING HABITS

The Quest would appear to be about breaking old habits and forming new ones, but the truth is that old habits don't really have to be broken. All that has to happen is that new behaviors assert themselves. For example, if you have a habit of turning left when you leave your home, you don't have to "break" the left-turn habit. All you have to do is practice new behavior—turn right! Given enough right turns, this will automatically replace the old behavior. (Practice, practice, practice!)

Your present use of your I AM is a habit. If you are dissatisfied with how you are using it, all that you have to do is replace the words you link with "I am" to words that more closely mirror your Christ essence.

1. Is there an area of your life about which you traditionally have had trouble being positive? Perhaps it's your intelligence or your finances or your self-image. *Make a list of all these "trouble" areas.*

For example: "I feel less intelligent than my family and friends."

"I doubt I'll ever get ahead financially."

"I have a history of bad relationships. I always end up making the wrong choice."

Make the list as exhaustive as possible.

2. Chances are that you have been using your I AM power to continually reaffirm these alleged weaknesses. *Make a list of statements you have used in the past to reaffirm these areas, and note the occasions on which you last used them.*

For example: "I was riding in a car with Allen and Joe and I hadn't read the newspaper story that they were discussing. When they asked me what I thought, I was embarrassed at not knowing, so I said, '*I am so ignorant* about financial matters.' "

List as many incidents as you can.

3. *Rethink each incident. What could you have said, using your I AM power, that would have been better than what you did say?*

For example: "When Joe and Allen asked my opinion, I could have said, 'I didn't read that article, but *I am happy* to hear you two discuss it.'"

Make sure you are using your I AM the way you mean to.

4. There are many times throughout each day that you do use your I AM in a positive way. *Make a list of all the areas in your life about which you feel very positive.*

For example: "I eat properly and exercise regularly, and I feel good about my health."

Make another list of the statements that you have used in the past to reaffirm your feelings about these areas. As in #2, also note the occasions on which you last used them.

For example: "I was with Mary and she was complaining about her health. I said, 'Mary, ever since I began exercising, *I am feeling better and better.* Why don't you try it?' "

WHAT DO YOU THINK OF ME?

Accepting others' opinions of us and attaching our I AM to these assessments is as harmful as initiating our own negative opinions of ourselves. We so often take someone's "you are" and make it our "I am."

All of his life, Jimmy heard from his mother, "Poor Jimmy, you are such a slow learner." It made perfect sense to him to think, I am Jimmy. I am a slow learner.

Judy grew up skinny and not very pretty. Now she is quite attractive. But the message she heard throughout her childhood and the one she still believes is: "Judy, you're so scrawny. You'll never be as pretty as your sister." I am Judy. I am ugly.

Bill, an African-American, grew up experiencing all of the subtle and often not-too-subtle messages of racial discrimination. It had a lasting impression on him. I am Bill. I am inferior.

5. *What message or messages of others have you adopted as your own? What have you allowed to attach itself to your I AM? List all of the messages that you have accepted throughout your life and have identified with your I AM.*

6. *How many of these messages do you still use with your I AM? List them all.*

What messages can you substitute?

7. It's been said that if you want to learn a new word, if you want to make it your own, use it three different times in a day.

Create an "I am" statement for every day this week that addresses any area of concern. Write it on enough index cards each day to tape onto bathroom mirrors, refrigerators, automobile dashboards, and anyplace else that will remind you to use it at least ten times that day.

OFF THE MAIN TRAIL

In one night of television viewing, keep a notebook beside you and write down all of the "I am" statements. Note how many of them are negative and how many are positive. If you are working with a Quest *group, discuss the results.*

STEPPING-STONE

Allow others to serve you. Feel good about receiving.

This is a real challenge for some of us. Whether our unwillingness to receive comes from a sense of unworthiness or stubbornness is hard to say, but many people do have difficulty accepting their good.

Feel good about receiving your meal from the waitress or waiter serving you, or from whoever serves you at home. Feel good about receiving service from a clerk at a store. Feel good about receiving a compliment or a gift. Feel good about the trash collector who removed your trash. Observe the different ways in which you are served or blessed by others. Feel good about receiving. Do it graciously and gratefully.

You are loved.

RELEASE AND AFFIRMATION

You've got to AC-CEN-TUATE THE POS-I-TIVE,
  Eliminate the negative,
Latch on to the affirmative,
  Don't mess with Mister In-between.
                    —Song by Johnny Mercer

Can you picture training wheels on a child's bike? Two small wheels attached to the back axle give stability to the bicycle so that anyone learning to ride won't fall over. Now consider the term *spiritual training wheels* in describing release and acceptance. We think it's a good analogy.

While learning to ride a bicycle, training wheels help you fine-tune your natural sense of balance without getting hurt by falling over. Spiritually, too, you may need assistance to fine-tune your balance. Too many experiences have the potential to knock you off your spiritual center. A harsh word, a deep disappointment, a nagging fear, these and a thousand other events can throw you off track. A simple statement of Truth principle can pull you back to your center, rebalance you spiritually.

SOUL-TALK

     Have you recognized that each *Soul-Talk* you've been encountering is an affirmation? If you've been faithfully using them throughout your quest, you realize how well they serve as signposts to keep you on the high road.

    This is one of the few Adventures where we're not going to give you *Soul-Talk*. You're going to create your own. When you've completed Activity 3, you'll come back here and write your statements of release and your affirmations three times each.

Release:

1. _____

2. _____

3. _____

Affirmation:

1. _____

2. _____

3. _____

_____

SOUL-THOUGHT

We thought it might be helpful to you if we listed some of our favorite statements of release and affirmation. Maybe they'll give you some ideas for your own. Remember: Release tears down, acceptance builds up. Release (denial) destructs, affirmation constructs. They both serve a purpose.

STATEMENTS OF RELEASE:

This, too, shall pass.

I don't need this in my life.

I release this from my life.

I don't accept this.

I won't.

Out!

Never!

Stop!

No!

STATEMENTS OF AFFIRMATION:

Everything is all right.

God is my source.

God is my health.

God is my help.

I can do it.

I am strong.

God is taking care of it.

I trust God.

It's all right.

Yes!

Now it's time to make up your own statements of release and affirmation. One good, strong release and one powerful affirmation based on Truth are all you ever really need at any given time, but you do need them both. The best are ones you can easily memorize and instantly call on in an emergency.

Important:

1. Make your statements short and to the point.

2. Choose vivid, descriptive words.

3. Be original and personal.

Statements of release and affirmation work better when they're your own. Once in a while you may find someone else's statement which just seems to "click" with you, but usually the ones you yourself create will mean more to you. This makes them more personally powerful and, therefore, better able to change your life.

Release and affirmation are tools to expand your consciousness, but if they don't have strong meaning for you, they're not going to work. Also, don't let their simplicity deceive you. They are powerful and effective "spiritual training wheels" to steady you until you find your divine equilibrium. Take advantage of them.

Let's work first on creating a statement of release. This usually appeals most to people who have a vivid memory and who tend to dwell on the past, especially past troubles. Also, assertive and self-confident people usually find releasing very effective and are likely to rely more on it than on accepting.

In creating your own release statement, it's good to remember what you want to accomplish. You're trying to break up old thinking, thinking thick with the accumulation of years of hardened belief about a situation. Encrusted thinking demands a powerful, very pointed statement of release to break it up. The best tool for breaking through concrete is a pickax. This sharply pointed tool puts the maximum amount of pressure on the smallest area, breaking up the hardened material much more quickly than a broad-faced hammer could ever do.

It's the same with your release. A short, very pointed, sharply directed statement proclaimed with passion has a powerful impact on your thought patterns, especially when backed by your conviction and emotion.

Personal Memo: Whenever our own thinking is not what we want, the best release statement for us is usually a strong, emotional, unequivocally blatant *No!* When circumstances permit us to bellow it out, so much the better. We do this in our home and in our car. However, you have our assurance that we do manage to restrain ourselves in a restaurant or a concert hall, when discretion dictates that we say it only to ourselves! But that's still okay because, fortunately, silent release works just as well, as long as it's done with feeling.

1. *Make up three strong, true, and meaningful statements of release appropriate to your present situation.* Keep them short and to the point. *Do this now before proceeding.*

a. _____

b. _____

c. _____

AFFIRMATION

Now that you have three good "weed killers," it's time to plant some flowers.

While we all need affirmations, people who tend to feel timid, fearful, and ineffectual, find them especially helpful. Affirmations also seem to work particularly well for those who feel they "give in" easily, who are doubting and anxious, or who are passive and lack confidence.

You know from the last Teaching the extraordinary power of the phrase "I am," so you can imagine how effective it is to begin your affirmation with these words. "I am," followed by what you are accepting, leaves no doubt as to what you are claiming for yourself.

Personal Memo: You may have guessed by now that our favorite affirmation is *Yes!* Whenever we think of what we're trying to accomplish, or whenever we think of God or good or peace or love or any of the positive emotions, we affirm with as much enthusiasm as we can muster, *Yes! Yes! Yes!* It's amazing how this utterly simple affirmation can bolster and reinforce that positive thought or feeling. Try it yourself.

2. *Make up three powerful, true, and positive affirmations appropriate to your present situation.* Keep them short and easy to say.

a. _____

b. _____

c. _____

If one technique, release or affirmation, is more meaningful to you than the other, do not use it exclusively. Although you may want to use one more than the other, both a release *and* an affirmation should be used regularly.

3. *Now select the one release and the one affirmation which have the most meaning for you.*
My release is: _____
My affirmation is: _____
  Memorize them both.

4. *Now go back and do your* Soul-Talk *and* Soul-Thoughts.

OFF THE MAIN TRAIL

The Gospels are rich with statements of release and affirmation used by Jesus. Find at least three of each and write them down, along with an explanation of the purpose for which He used them.

Hint: A red letter version of the Bible will be a major help to you, because Jesus' words are highlighted.

Whenever you think of any present challenge, immediately repeat your release three times. Follow it with your affirmation three times.

In addition, repeat your affirmation whenever you think of it.

"Yes, but that means I could be saying each of them hundreds of times a day."

Exactly! That's just what you want to do: flush out the old dysfunctional thoughts and feelings and coax your consciousness to accept the good that God wants for you. Repeat them as often as you can— silently, if necessary, but aloud when possible—until they become so much a part of you that they spring to mind automatically. That's when they do their finest work.

Note: If you do this faithfully, it's going to point out to you just how much time and energy you've been wasting on useless thoughts and feelings. This can be a shocking revelation, but since you are serious about changing, you'll be grateful for the opportunity to work on this. Good statements of release and affirmation will prove to be true friends on your quest. Use them lavishly.

MOVING INTO ACTION

Even if you're on the right track, you'll get run over if you just sit there.

—Will Rogers

There are two ways to get to the top of an oak tree. One way is to sit on an acorn and pray and wait.

Hippocrates said, "Prayer indeed is good, but while calling on the gods a man should himself lend a hand." In other words, if you really want to get to the top of the oak tree, climb it.

MOVEMENT BRINGS IMPROVEMENT

It may seem contradictory to think of moving into action when, a short time ago, you not only admitted you were powerless but you then went on to totally surrender! How does admitting personal powerlessness and surrendering fit into the concept of moving into action?

Actually, the concepts are not mutually exclusive. As you know, saying that you are personally powerless is not admitting complete impotence; surrendering is not quitting. Both of these steps are designed to help you disengage from the problem, not from the solution. Plus, admitting personal helplessness and surrendering to God are both actions.

Because the power of God works through you, you are a co-creator with God. As we said before, God has no hands or feet or vocal cords. You do. You can, by your actions, change your world. True, all actions begin with a thought but, without action, thoughts can tend to dissipate themselves into nothingness.

Wheat kernels found in an Egyptian tomb were still alive after many thousands of years, still capable of growing. It was estimated that if they had been planted and their seeds replanted from then until now, those few original seeds would have yielded enough wheat to feed the entire world. Like the wheat kernels in the tomb—rich in potential but poor in yield— thoughts, too, will lie fallow when not translated into action.

Thoughts are powerful, but actions are powerful too. Think of eating a meal. Depending on how hungry you are, you can begin to salivate just anticipating it. No matter how much you think of the meal, if you don't eat it, if you don't take action, you will not be nourished. Yes, thoughts are powerful, but they must be transformed into actions in order to reach the full potential of their power.

SOUL-TALK

God directs my actions.

1. _____

2. _____

3. _____

SOUL-THOUGHTS

THOUGHTS, EMOTIONS, ACTIONS

In order to have meaningful change in your life, you have to set into motion the truth that you've already taken into your heart. A bodybuilder can stare at his weights for days with the thought that they will improve his physique. It's only when he takes action, when he begins lifting those weights, that muscles develop.

Yet *actions* will not be effective unless they begin with a *thought* and are energized by an *emotion*, by a feeling. Thoughts, emotions, and actions. *All* are needed.

Thoughts Alone: What if the only change in your life is a thought? Then there can be no change. This is the domain of the dreamer. It is the world of the person who lives a life of "if only." "I could find the perfect woman if only I were more outgoing." "I would feel more secure if only I were richer." "If only I had a different job I would be happier." "I would feel less stressed if only my son would get better grades."

Emotions Alone: What would happen if you tried to change your life using emotions only? Emotions alone are also ineffective. Emotions, even strong emotions, are not enough to change anything. People are frozen in the emotion of fear, incapacitated by the emotion of anger, overcome with the emotion of grief. An emotion, if it is strong enough, can immobilize you. Emotions can lift you up or slam you down, but alone, they cannot permanently change your world.

Actions Alone: Actions alone are just as futile. Running here and there, jumping into things without thinking them out, and acting in an "off-in-all-direc-tions" way is hollow motion. It wastes a lot of time and energy and offers no permanent rewards. Such behavior is worthless in changing you in any meaningful or lasting way. A windup toy is an example of pure action without thought or emotion.

Thought and Action: Even if two of the three are combined, there can be no meaningful change. For example, if you have a thought linked with action, it won't last. An emotion is needed as the spark plug to keep the action going; otherwise, your actions just fizzle. (How many times have you made a New Year's resolution with no real emotion behind it, only to have your changes fade out by February? You had the thought and you took the action, but you could not sustain it because the proper emotion was missing.) Nothing major ever happens in our lives unless a strong emotion is attached to it.

Emotion and Action: If you link an emotion and an action with no thought, you are out of control. This is the world of the addict. "If it feels good, do it." This is the person who takes action without evaluating the consequences of his actions. This is the person who "*reacts*" to circumstances rather than *acting* from thought.

Thought and Emotion: How about a thought linked with an emotion? That is as futile as the impatient motorcyclist stopped at a traffic light, gunning his engine again and again. He knows where he wants to go and is impatient to get there, but there is no movement toward his goal.

Thoughts, Emotions, and *Actions:* We need all three. To grow and change in a spiritually sound and emotionally mature way, thought and emotion and action must all be joined together as one. When there is inspired *thought* linked with loving and enthusiastic *emotion* followed by appropriate *action,* we can't help but change our world for the better.

1. *Whatever specific challenge you are working on, have you admitted personal powerlessness over it?*

Have you surrendered?

If you are satisfied that you are *personally* powerless to improve your life and if you have surrendered to God, you are ready to take action, but this time you *know* that the outcome will be beneficial to you.

In the past, maybe you weren't quite sure and so your actions could have been tentative and tinged with doubt. You've probably experienced the feeling. It's like driving to a destination not quite sure that the road you are taking is the right one. You are hesitant in your decisions and never go full speed because there is always a nagging worry that all may not turn out well. But once you know you're on the right road, you go full speed, secure in the knowledge that all is well. It's a good feeling.

If you have turned your life with all of its challenges over to God, you are on the right road. All is well, and that's a great feeling!

2. The best way to gauge a change is to compare the present with something from the past which hasn't changed. (Ever notice how your clothes tell you if your weight has changed?)

Using as many people or circumstances as you can think of from the past, compare the way you interact with them now with the way you acted in the past.

For example, compare the way you treated a difficult neighbor in the past with the way you treat him or her now. Or compare how you used to react to a traffic jam and how you react now. Or how do your present actions compare to your actions in the past when dealing with a healing need you may have?

For each person or circumstance, answer the following questions:

a. *Are you acting differently?*

b. *If so, how have your actions changed?*

c. *If you are not acting differently than you did in the past, has your thinking really changed?* (In fact, if you are not acting differently than in the past, it may be a cue that you're not really sure of the direction. It would be worthwhile to give this some thought.)

d. *If your thinking has changed but your actions haven't, what can you do to change your actions so that they correspond with your thoughts?* Perhaps you should look at the emotion attached to that thought.

3. *Spend time each day while on this Adventure reviewing the last twenty-four hours. Be thorough. Make a list of the actions you took which you are proud of.*

(For example: "I responded kindly to Ralph although he said nasty things to me." Or, "I replaced most negative thoughts about my son's divorce with positive ones.") *You will write these daily reviews in your separate notebook.*

I am proud of these actions:

Now make another list of actions you took that you are less than proud of.

("Blasted horn impatiently at slow car in front of me." Or, "Worried about arthritis.")

Next time I'll take more positive action with these:

4. *Think of the area or areas of your life that you want changed. For each area, answer the following questions:*

What is the present thought? Is the goal clear to you?

What is the present emotion? *Do you have a positive emotion coupled with this thought, or are fear and anxiety involved? Identify the emotion.*

What is the present action? *Judging from what you have learned so far on your journey, are your actions appropriate? Describe them.*

5. *Analyze your answers. For each answer, do the following:*

Thought—*If the thought is not clear, change it. Write a clearer goal.*

Emotion—*If the emotion is less than positive, change it. Write down what you believe would be an appropriate emotion and then work at really feeling it and incorporating it into your thinking.*

Action—*If the action is contrary to your goal, change it. Write down the actions you feel will bring you most directly to your goal.*

OFF THE MAIN TRAIL

Choose a book, fairy tale, movie, play, short story, or Bible story. How does the leading character (the hero or heroine) move into action to change the course of his or her life?

How did this action help the character attain a

goal? What was the transformation which took place in the character?

What "treasure" did he or she attain?

STEPPING-STONE

Be as aware as possible of any opportunity to act in a new and exciting way, and then take action.

Even a trip to the supermarket or gas station is ripe with possibility of growth if each thought, each encounter, each transaction is anchored in an outer deed which reflects your inner spiritual changes. The key is to be aware, to be awake to the possibilities.

This will take concentration, but habits—good habits in this case—are developed by repetition. The more you take action, the deeper the thought is "grooved" into your brain and the more likely you will be to repeat it.

This is a *Stepping-Stone* that should be retained even after this Adventure is completed and you have begun the next Teaching. This is a lifetime *Stepping-Stone*, but you won't mind at all because it's so rewarding.

God directs your actions.

If I keep a green branch in my heart, the singing bird will come.

—Chinese Proverb

Faith works. What you expect, you get. That's wonderful to know, because you've been given free will and can choose what to expect! You can make the decision to expect good, which is what God's will is for you. Good is actually everywhere around you, just waiting to be expected so that it can become part of your life.

But watch out, fear can keep that good from you. Fear is one of those dragons along the path that blocks your good. Yet, what is fear? Simply, faith pointed in the wrong direction.

You have an unlimited amount of faith within you. We've already talked about that in the Guidebook. Now is a good time to take a look at how you are investing that faith. Where are you putting it? On a problem, giving that problem even more power, or on the solution—on God?

It's vital for you to know that where your faith is, there is your power. It's that simple.

1. *Reread the true stories of the man using the drug and the girl at Lourdes. Describe how each one's faith was involved in the outcome.*

The man using the drug:

The girl at Lourdes:

Now carefully examine your own faith. Where is it leading? Is it focused on an appearance or on the truth? In other words, is your thinking fixed on the problem (what you see and hear) or on the solution (God)?

If you don't change the direction of your faith, you'll end up exactly where you are heading! That's why it's important to check out what you are expecting, what occupies most of your thinking, and about what it is that you're continually talking. That's where your faith is.

2. *What do you expect?* A good way to find out is to analyze what you talk about most. Ask your Spiritual Support Group how much you talk about your problem. (And give them permission to be honest with you!)

How often do you discuss this problem or situation with others?

What did you say the last time you discussed it? Write out as much as you can remember.

3. *Be aware of your thinking.* Watch for the signs which are dead giveaways that you are misdirecting your faith. For example, you might find yourself saying "my stiff fingers," which shows you're staking a claim on it for yourself. Or "I'll never be able to afford that," a surefire way to send your prosperity to the gallows. It's so easy to repeat things you don't really mean, not realizing how you're herding your faith into the wrong pasture by saying them. *Write out some of the things you normally say which indicate a misdirected faith.*

4. Do you really mean what you've been saying? Probably not. *So now rewrite each statement in a positive, faith-filled way.* (For example, if you wrote, "I'm so lonely," you might write, "I'm attracting new friends.")

Your first statements were signs of misplaced faith, good faith squandered in wrong directions. They're a signal to you to redirect your faith toward only good. Staying aware of what you say can help.

BELIEVING IS SEEING

Do you want to know how easy it is to misplace faith? We've all done it. It's the easiest thing in the world, because we're brought up in a society which often likes to accentuate the negative. If we don't take steps to associate mainly with positive people, we can find ourselves surrounded by "crepehangers," those who like to turn every situation into a funeral. Here are some cases of misplaced faith which then was redirected.

An uncle of ours was doing battle with a health challenge. (If you've ever had a serious illness, you know only too well how easy it is to stay caught up in worry and fear.) His faith was very strong, but it was invested in terrible fear and anxiety. What is it that he was expecting? Then one day he had a revelation. He describes it as a "bolt out of the blue!" He suddenly realized that he had to shift his faith to the belief that God is more powerful than any appearance of disease or disharmony in his body. He caught the idea that *God's desire for him is absolute good*—and that includes wholeness. He didn't just think it. He *knew* it. He had faith in it. He *believed* he was being healed. And he was.

It is very easy to have faith in something you have already experienced. After all, seeing is believing. Yet that's not faith, that's just plain common sense. With true faith, believing is seeing! In other words, having faith is seeing your good *before* it comes into your life, and that's what our uncle was able to do.

HER FAITH CHANGED THE OUTCOME

Here's another real-life example of misplaced faith

that you might be able to identify with. A close friend of ours secretly feared and believed that her relationship with her mother-in-law would never be any good. She confessed that she'd been pouring her faith into all kinds of undesirable results, exactly what she didn't want. Strong faith, again, but it was faith in things never getting any better. What was she expecting? a lifetime of bitterness and resentment between her and her husband's mother, and that's exactly what she was getting.

But, all's well that ends well, and we're happy to report that today our friend has moved her mother-in-law into their garage apartment and the two have become very close! What happened? It's a long story, but it ended with our friend's discovery that God was in charge of her situation! She really came to believe that, and once she believed it, her faith was invested in expecting the perfect solution for the situation. All her efforts—both physical and mental—were directed toward expecting good. This expectation, this faith, provided a channel through which God could express.

It works that way for everyone. You can see it in your own life. As soon as your faith is placed where it belongs, God's perfect plan can begin to unfold. Keep in mind that God's plan is always better than anything you could have imagined. That same strong faith which you had aimed in the wrong direction will now be turned around and aimed toward the truth, toward God. Fortunately, God *always* knows how to work things out perfectly.

CHANGE POSITIONS, CHANGE CONDITIONS

When you change the position of your faith, you will change the condition of your life. You will be led to the people, places, and things that will help you. It's all part of God at work in your life. Change the location of your faith, and you will change the climate of your life.

Are you concerned about someone else? If you truly want God's highest good for that person, invest your faith in expecting that good. Strongly believe that no disease or way of life or mental attitude can wreck that person's life. Know with every cell of your body that God dwells within each person and is guiding that person toward his or her good.

It's not always easy. When you see your loved one in physical or emotional pain or heading in a seemingly disastrous direction, it's very easy to get swept up in the negativity of the situation and to expect the worst. Yet this is exactly the time when your faith has to be pushed and prodded toward solid ground, so that you actually expect the right thing to happen for him or her. "Yes, but my situation is different," you might protest. "I can't expect anything good to come out of *this*!" But you can.

Get in the habit of continually checking out your faith. Where does it lie? Regular meditation will make you aware of God's infinite presence and power and wisdom. This awareness will help you to keep your faith where it should be: on your good.

The purpose of this teaching is to help you understand that no matter what kind of situation is in your life today, the solution is to *know* and *expect* that God will lead you through it to your good. This kind of faith is your only solid-gold guarantee of success.

THE NATURE OF FAITH

You will always find faith linked to an emotion. That is its nature. In fact, faith without an emotion is hollow. Trouble is, it's just as easy to attach it to a negative emotion as it is a positive one. Belief in the negative, expecting the worse, makes for a really powerful faith, and as you know, what you strongly expect, you get! Let's explore this further.

5. *Become still for a few minutes. As you relax, bring to mind as vividly as you can a past situation where you were fearful or anxious. Recall the feelings you experienced at the time. Allow them free rein as you relive the event. Go ahead and do this now.*

How did you feel? What about your faith? Was it pointed in the wrong direction? Isn't it obvious that this had choked the flow of God's plan? You had actually blocked the good which was supposed to have come to you. Well, enough of that. Let's move on.

6. *Let that memory fade as you relax completely. Now remember a time when you felt on top of the world. You knew that everything was going to go perfectly. You expected it, and that is precisely what happened. Recall that now, again allowing your feelings free rein.*

What were your *feelings* at the time? Vividly recall some scenes from that situation. What emotions were involved? Feel them now as you relive the experience. You had absolute faith that the outcome was going to be wonderful, didn't you? And, naturally, it was.

7. *Continue to sit quietly, holding on to those feelings of great expectation and elation. Now transfer those feelings to your present situation. Feel the marvelous joy and comfort of knowing God is taking care of*

things for you. Have you caught the feeling? Now *that* is the Jesus Christ kind of faith.

As you rise and go about your daily activities, make a real effort to continually experience those wonderful feelings which whisper in your soul, "God is in charge. Everything is all right!"

SOUL-TALK

You've no doubt noticed by now that *Soul-Talk* is not in its usual place this time. From now on you will be consciously redirecting your faith, moving it immediately back to God whenever you catch it looking in the wrong direction. The more you practice this, the easier it becomes. Affirmations will really help you with this. This is intentional.

Here are some we've found to be effective. You may want to make up more, but for now *select the one which has the strongest appeal to you. Repeat it silently and aloud as often as you can—hundreds of times a day, if necessary—until it becomes part of you. Get it into your very tissues. Work with it until you can feel its power.*

> *God is taking care of it.*
>
> *My good is on its way.*
>
> *Everything is all right.*
>
> *God can do it.*
>
> *I expect only good.*
>
> *My faith is in God.*
>
> *This, too, shall pass.*
>
> *The best is yet to be.*
>
> *God is at work.*

Great things are happening.

Write the statement you have selected. This will be your Soul-Talk *for this Adventure.*

My *Soul-Talk* is _____

1. _____

2. _____

3. _____

SOUL-THOUGHTS

OFF THE MAIN TRAIL

 Take a scrupulous inventory of your own faith in each area of your life. What are you expecting?
Health:

Finances:

Relationships:

Personal satisfaction:

Profession:

Concern for someone else:

Other:

Honestly search your soul to assess the direction and type of faith you are using in each of these areas. Write down your evaluations.

STEPPING-STONE

Each evening take a mental tally of your faith investments for the day.

Many of us spend more time checking out our financial investments than we do the investments of our faith. As you take a tally each evening, do you find most of your faith investments on the asset (positive) side or on the debit (negative) side? Where were your expectations each day? Add them up and see which side has the larger total.

What is your score? Do the daily totals show that your faith is invested in fear or in God? Your assignment is to increase your asset score.

The best is yet to be.

FORGIVENESS

After a good dinner, one can forgive anyone,
even one's own relatives.

—Oscar Wilde

All seagoing boats have one problem in common: barnacles! These small creatures attach themselves to the hulls, adding weight and increasing the turbulence. This slows down the speed of the boat.

As the barnacles grow larger and as more attach themselves, the boat is less able to perform until, if allowed to accumulate indefinitely, the barnacles will disable the boat completely. Wise captains know that periodically they must remove their boats from the water and scrape off the barnacles.

As we "sail" through life we, too, acquire "barnacles." However, we acquire them on our soul, on our consciousness! What are these barnacles? The biggest ones are the resentments and hatreds and unforgivenesses which mentally "weigh us down," increasing the amount of turbulence in our lives.

These barnacles slow down the speed of our spiritual progress.

It is up to us to routinely "scrape the barnacles," to forgive those whom we've judged to be unworthy of our love. God's love is the gentle blowing breeze which can take us as far as we want to go, but if we are allowing barnacles of unforgiveness to cling to us, we can't raise our consciousness to take advantage of this love. Only by forgiving can we move forward on our spiritual path, unencumbered and unburdened by the barnacles of resentment and unforgiveness.

SOUL-TALK

 Love fills my heart.

1. _____

2. _____

3. _____

SOUL-THOUGHTS

Note: As you begin the second half of your Quest, be sure you are spending quality time on your *Soul-Thoughts*, using this section to record any impressions you are aware of, any changes you feel are important in your life. Continue to make *Soul-Thoughts* your log, an accurate record of your unfoldment. The more time you spend on this section, especially in this second half of *The Quest*, the richer and more rewarding will be your experience.

"LOVE YOUR ENEMIES"

We can't really love until we forgive. Unforgiveness stands in the way of unconditional love and our decision to love is too important to relinquish to someone else, which is what we do when we resent or hate.

Loving is the most natural of all of our spiritual gifts, but because of our humanity it is not always easy, especially when someone dislikes us. Then our negative feelings restrain the expression of our love. There is only one solution and that is to love the person with whom we are having difficulty. Jesus' admonishment to us was to "love your enemies." Why? Because *the power inherent in our divinity is available only when we love.* If we allow someone, anyone, to cause us not to love him or her, we allow that person to take our power.

Note the words *Love* your *enemies.* Why did

Jesus not just say "Love enemies"? It was because there is really no such thing as an "enemy"! Enemies are how *we* define another person. They are always "our" enemies.

"STICKS AND STONES ..."

In truth, we have no enemies, no matter how others have treated us. There are two reasons for this: First of all, the other person, like you, is a spiritual being. He or she can act cruelly, but that person's spiritual nature is always intact. Just as the sun can be hidden behind monsoon rain clouds, a person's divinity can be hidden behind hideous acts. But one day the clouds will disperse and the sun will shine again. It always does.

The second truth is that because we are spiritual beings, we cannot be harmed by the words, opinions, or actions of another. We can be cut and bruised physically; we can be hurt on a human level by verbal abuse from another. But who we *really* are is untouched and can never be influenced by another person. Knowing who and what we really are frees us from the belief that the *real* of us has been injured. "Sticks and stones can break my bones but names can never define my spiritual nature."

These are two important spiritual truths. Other people are spiritual beings unaffected at their essence by their own words or deeds. You, at your essence, are a spiritual being and are unaffected at a spiritual level by others' opinions or actions.

"ISOMETRIC" FORGIVENESS

Before going on to our Forgiveness Meditation, a

word about the importance of *trying* to forgive. We are aware that the decision to forgive can be quite a challenge for some people. Even after one decides to forgive, implementing that decision is often even more difficult. We may feel that someone has hurt us so grievously that we just can't bring ourselves to forgive. We may have considered it but are just not ready to do it. That's understandable. The spiritual path can be a difficult one, and we do the best we can where we are.

It is the *willingness* to forgive which is the important gesture. A sincere desire to forgive is almost as beneficial as actually forgiving.

You've probably heard the term *isometric exercise.* Isometric exercises involve no movement. Muscle pressure is exerted against a stationary object, such as standing in a doorway and pushing intensely against both doorjambs. Although there is no movement, there is a great deal of muscle exertion and, therefore, muscle development. Think of it. If every day you tried hard to lift your car, there would obviously be no movement of the car. Yet in spite of the fact that the car did not move, you would have strengthened your muscles more and more by just *trying* to move it.

It's much the same with *trying* to forgive someone. Each time you open yourself to forgiveness, you open yourself to Spirit. In trying to forgive, you are attempting to see this person as he or she is, a child of God fully as endowed with all good as you are.

Like isometric exercises, "isometric forgiveness" makes you spiritually stronger. The difference is that no matter how you struggle and strain trying to lift the car, you never will. But in trying to forgive someone, no matter how hopeless it may seem, as long as you keep at it and as long as you *want* to forgive, you will eventually succeed.

1. *Make a list of the people you want to forgive and choose the one person you feel you should forgive first. When you have forgiven that person, cross out his or her name and take on the next one.*

2. Intellectual understanding alone can't bring forgiveness because it is the intellect that initially judges someone as unforgivable. Only God can reveal to us who and what we are and who and what that other person is. The first work in forgiving, therefore, is to ask the God of love to reveal to us all that we are and all that this other person is.

Forgiveness Meditation

Say a prayer to center yourself as you get ready to do your Forgiveness Meditation. Let God know that you desire to truly forgive and then approach this time with a feeling of calm expectation. Know that you are going toward your good, and that as you forgive, you are reclaiming the power of love which you had temporarily relinquished.

Become quiet in your favorite meditation spot and give yourself a few moments to relax and go through

218

any meditation ritual that you normally do.

When you are ready, begin repeating silently over and over to yourself: Love fills my heart.

At some point in your meditation bring up the face of the person you want to forgive. Dispassionately and lovingly, see past the eyes to the soul of that person, recognizing the connection to God and to you.

If you have a visceral reaction to the face of the person and can't get past the hatred, visualize him or her as an infant—innocent, pure, incapable of hurting you. See past the eyes of that infant to its soul. Connect at that level and hold that vision as long as you can. Ask God to reveal to you who and what that person really is and who and what you are in relation to him or her. (If you find yourself rehashing the problem you have had with this person, gently bring your mind back to the phrase, Love fills my heart.*)*

When you are ready to finish your Forgiveness Meditation, speak the person's name aloud and say, "_____, I love you, I bless you, and I release you."

Spend a few minutes of quiet time before you get up from your chair.

OFF THE MAIN TRAIL

 Mehmet Ali Agca shot and seriously wounded Pope John Paul II in an attempted assassination. The Pope suffered much pain in his long rehabilitation. Yet a short time later, he went to visit Mehmet Ali Agca in his jail cell. The men sat closely together and spoke for a long time. When the Pope was ready to leave, he blessed Agca and the two men shook hands and embraced. Asked by reporters what was said, the Pope answered, "I spoke to him as I would speak to a brother whom I have forgiven."

Explain in detail what forgiveness has to do with the following statement: "The power that is part of our divinity is ours only when we love. If we allow someone, anyone, to cause us not to love him or her, we allow that person to take our power."

STEPPING-STONE

Write out a list of all the good traits of someone you don't like.

Every day choose a different person, relative, friend, acquaintance, TV personality, politician, anyone. On a separate sheet of paper, list everything that is good about this person. If you really dislike him or her, it may be difficult to find something good. However, if you persist you will find *something*, even if all you can list to begin with is that this person has a nice brother!

If you are having trouble with an organization, list it. It could be that you are in conflict with an insurance company about a claim or an automobile agency about a repair. Include it on your list. Unforgiveness doesn't have to be directed to an individual in order to be harmful to you.

Love fills your heart.

All you need is love.
　　—The Beatles

Everyone at a seminar was given a pack of little cards which read, "You are loved." Their assignment was simple: give away all of the cards over the weekend and, as you do, give the energy of your love with it.

Cards were put into letters, some were left with tips at restaurants, others were put anonymously in people's books and on their desks. The cards were symbols of love expressed, and everyone felt good getting one. It was the *givers*, however, who felt the best. To them, it was a renewal of a connection with love, and each time they left a card, they allowed this connection to become stronger—and it felt so good.

TYPES OF LOVE

There seem to be three main types of love. One can be called a sensual love. This is a love that is chiefly *self*-centered. It is love expressed for the sake of physical pleasure or personal fulfillment. It is a selfish love. "I love you only because it makes *me* feel good." We love someone else only to make us feel good, or we love someone in order to draw attention to ourselves. These kinds of relationships, based on sensual love, are doomed for disaster.

Another kind of love is conditional love. This is love based on a *quid pro quo.* "If you love me, I'll give you my love." Love is not given freely but is, in a sense, bartered. Loving or withholding love depends on whether and/or how the love is returned by another person.

The third kind of love, the purest form, is Christ love. This is love for the pure joy of loving. Christ love is completely unconditional and instinctive. It is love that recognizes it doesn't need anyone for it to bubble freely and spontaneously from the wellspring of all love, which is the presence of God within one. This is the love that Jesus taught and practiced. This is the love felt by the people who gave away those cards saying, "You are loved."

The essence of Christ love is: *"I am love."*

SOUL-TALK

I am love.

1. _____

2. _____

3. _____

THE ONLY LOVE IS LOVE EXPRESSED

Loving people don't strive for love, they allow love. If you think of the most loving people you know, chances are they are not *trying* to love. They are simply being true to what they are, and what they are *is* love.

Love expressed fully and unconditionally is the only love, yet not everyone always expresses such love. We too often allow others to fool us into thinking that we should withhold love from them. They put on masks of anger and assume postures of hatred to trick us into giving them only conditional love or, worse, no love at all!

Whenever people treat us in an obnoxious way,

it's important to love them. Certainly it's easy to judge them as not worthy of our love, but in withholding love from them, we are first depriving ourselves. Are we unworthy too?

If you are in doubt about loving someone, remember Jesus' admonition: "As you did it to one of the least of these my brethren, you did it to me" (Mt. 25:40).

The degree to which you can let your love flow unconditionally in all directions is the automatic built-in gauge of how you are letting God express in your life. Your love quotient is never higher than the least amount of love you give to some person, no matter how much you think you are loving someone else.

1. *How can you express more of the love you have? Be creative. Think of new ways to let love flow from you.*

2. *In the past, how has someone's love for you affected your decision to love that person and others?*

For example, the leader of a clique in high school may have shown love for you and you may have decided to love him and his group.

Choose and analyze one incident.

3. *In the past, how has someone's lack of love for you affected your decision to withhold love from that person and others?*

For example, a bitter divorce may have led you to withhold love from your former mate and his or her family.

Choose and analyze one incident.

4. *Do you now use a stuffed animal to help you release love or do you use a pet to help you express love? Discuss how these help you to do so.*

5. *Has the Forgiveness Meditation from the last Activity noticeably increased your ability to love? Explain why or why not.*

6. *Is there anyone you love unconditionally?*

Think about this for a good while. If you answered "yes," be sure there are no strings attached to your love. If you feel you could love this person more if he or she did something more, then your present love is conditional. Or if your love would diminish even a little bit if this person stopped doing something (like loving you), it is conditional.

7. *Do you feel you love yourself unconditionally?* Would you love yourself more if you lost some weight or stopped smoking or got a better job? *Discuss this.*

8. Please answer each of these next questions *spontaneously* as you read them and answer them in order.

List your three greatest assets. What do you feel makes you special or unusual? (Answer this now.)

a. _____

b. _____

c. _____

List your three greatest liabilities. What areas need improvement to make you a better person?

a. _____

b. _____

c. _____

What single thing are you most proud of?

What single thing are you most ashamed of?

If you could improve what you are proud of, would you feel more lovable?

If you could change what you are ashamed of, would you feel more lovable?

Analyze and discuss your answers.

9. On a "Love Scale" from -10 to +10, where would you rate your present love capacity? Put a mark where you feel it is. Do that now before reading any further.

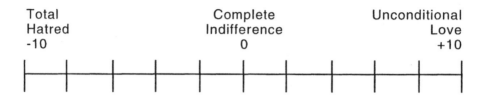

| Total
Hatred
-10 | | | | Complete
Indifference
0 | | | | Unconditional
Love
+10 |

10. On the same scale, put a mark on the spot that indicates your degree of love for the least lovable person in your life. Do that now before reading any further.

The degree to which you let your love flow unconditionally in *all* directions is the only gauge of how you are letting God express in your life. Your ability to love is indicated by your love toward the least lovable person in your life. Jesus said, "As you did it to one of the least of these my brethren, you did it to me."

That second mark represents your present love capacity right now. As you work on forgiving and loving more, this second mark will move to the right.

OFF THE MAIN TRAIL

In the Guidebook we stated: "Our soul's growth depends on how much of God's love we can accept. When we stop accepting and expressing love, we stop growing."

Explain this concept.

STEPPING-STONE

Act each day this week in terms of service.

Let "What can I do for others?" be your focus this week. You can start by being kind and supportive to others. Radiate your goodwill in all directions. Be like the floodlight not the spotlight. Don't wait for something on which to focus in order to be loving. Let love be *your* idea.

You are love.

GUIDANCE

He who builds according to every man's advice will have a crooked house.

—Danish Proverb

How can we be guided to act from our Christ centers? The same way a pilot is guided to land on the right runway—by being in contact with the person who has the overall view. In the case of the pilot, it is the air traffic controller in the tower. In our case, it is the Christ within us that always knows what's best for us, which has the overall view—the big picture. We maintain contact with our inner guidance, our Christ center, through prayer and meditation.

SOUL-TALK

I am divinely guided.

1. _____

2. _____

3. _____

_____

SOUL-THOUGHTS

_____

IT HAS TO "FEEL" RIGHT

Attorneys, accountants, financial planners, ministers, counselors, advisors, and others can help us in making important decisions. Yet no matter how many agree, no decision is the right decision until it feels right inside of us. No matter how many people tell us what we "should" do, if we are prayed up and don't feel right doing it, we shouldn't do it. More than any other benchmark in deciding if a decision is the right decision (after we have prayed about it), is the feeling of joy attached to it. This usually means it's right.

OUR PERSONAL RULE

For the most part, however, our own favorite rule for reading signs is what we like to call our "open-door policy." It's our policy that if we are undecided about several options and a door to one of those options opens, even a little bit, we go through it. We make it a habit to continue going through only those doors which are open, only those doors that feel good and which we can sail through smoothly.

1. Adventure 13, Activity 2 asked if you have ever made a decision that you felt was God's will. Go back and review your answer. Describe in detail the feelings you had before and after you made the decision.

2. Identify an important decision you made that you were not quite sure was a God-guided decision.

Describe in detail the feelings you had before and

after you made an important decision you were not sure of.

     3. *What is the single most important decision you have to make now?*

     Can you identify any open doors? Write them down.

What doors seem closed to you?

Discuss the pros and cons in detail.

4. In the Guidebook we said that the four prereq-
uisites for a good decision were *release, openness,
trust,* and a feeling of *peace.* Check yourself out on all
four of these factors:

Release—*To what extent have you released the
outcome?* Do you feel that God is in charge, and that
as long as you are centered in prayer, everything will
be all right? (If not, it may be a good idea to reread
Teachings 15 and 16.)

Discuss this in detail.

Openness—*Are you open to any outcome, not just the one that you feel is the right one?*

As honestly as you can, discuss your feelings about this.

Trust—*Do you trust that God will guide you to do what's best for you?*

Although it may be difficult to admit that you don't fully trust God, write at length about your feelings on this matter.

Peace—*Are you feeling peaceful about the eventual outcome? Discuss this in the space provided.*

ARE YOU PRAYED UP?

Have you been doing your prayer work? In asking for guidance, it's important that you be prayed up, to be open and receptive to God's guidance. Rather than analyzing everything that happens in your life, use the exceptionally effective prayer: "God, speak to me in a way I cannot possibly ignore." If you can say this prayer in faith, you will be able to release the outcome of your present challenge and know that God's guidance will be clear and unequivocal, and that you will be directed to the perfect action on your part.

End each prayer session with that statement. You will find it a great comfort.

OFF THE MAIN TRAIL

The decision-making process often goes through much intellectual evaluation before we feel frustrated enough or free enough to seek guidance from the Christ within. Yet there has to be the component of intellectual analysis in every decision we make. *Discuss this seeming contradiction that on one hand dictates we use common sense to make decisions and on the other hand, directs us to look to the Christ within for our guidance.*

STEPPING-STONE

Pray for a different "enemy" every day.

A few Activities ago your *Stepping-Stone* was to pray for your friends. That was, no doubt, enjoyable and uplifting. This week may be a bit more challenging. Each day choose someone you are having trouble loving and pray for that person. It could be someone you know personally, someone with whom you work or possibly a neighbor. It may be someone you were very close to at one time, like a former husband or wife and with whom you now feel an enmity. Maybe your "enemy" is a parent who treated you cruelly when you were a child. Perhaps it is someone only known to you, like the owner of your apartment who just raised your rent or the adjuster of the insurance company who refuses to approve your claim. Give your choices careful consideration. The more you feel you are in opposition to them, the more *you* need to pray for them.

Whomever you choose to pray for each day, it is not necessary to tell him or her. Just actively include each of them, a different one every day, in your thoughts and prayers.

You are divinely guided.

OVERCOMING FEAR

Fear knocked on the door. Faith answered.
No one was there.

—Author unknown

"I am the Lord your God .... You shall have no other gods before me" (Ex. 20:2-3). But not to worry. All of the golden calves have been destroyed. People don't worship false gods anymore, do they?

Or do they? Think about this: If you are fearful of something—illness, old age, criticism, poverty, flying, death—aren't you giving that object of fear more power than you are giving to God? Isn't this fear really a "false god" that you have put before God?

You see, fear is really the negative use of faith. In worshiping at the negative altar of fear rather than the positive altar of faith, we are indeed breaking that first commandment and "glorifying" something other than God.

SOUL-TALK

God is in charge of my life.

1. _____

2. _____

3. _____

SOUL-THOUGHTS

LET THE DOMINOES FALL

A friend of ours was ravaged with fears. This included a fear of flying, of tunnels, of bridges, of high places, of speaking in public, of being alone, of small rooms, of sitting in front of a classroom, of germs, of sickness, of dying, and countless more. In fact, there were few things of which she was not afraid. Finally, when her fears got so restrictive that she could barely exist, she decided to tackle the biggest fear she had—fear of flying.

With much prayer preparation and moral support from her family, she agreed to have a friend take her up in his small airplane. Her constant affirmation from the time she decided to do it until she landed was: *God is in charge.*

Although she didn't enjoy the flight, she did take off, circle the airport, and land. One small step for humankind but a giant leap for our friend. The really amazing thing, however, is that within six months after this flight, she was virtually free of all of her other fears!

There is a curious phenomenon which occurs when we make the first breakthrough of our fears. There is a domino reaction. As the first fear falls, it has a tendency to topple the next, and then the next, until finally the once-threatening brigade of fears is now lying helpless, stripped of its power and no longer capable of ruling our lives.

1. *What is the biggest fear in your life right now?*

2. *When you conquer this fear, what other fears will eventually crumble?* List them all. Also describe the reason they will disappear.

244

3. *Prepare yourself for a quiet meditative experience.*

Sitting in a comfortable chair, slowly read this statement aloud three times: I open my mind to divine wisdom. All fears dissolve. Whatever inner changes I must make are revealed to me.

Sitting quietly and breathing easily, allow yourself to think of a situation which would involve facing your biggest fear. When you have a scene clearly in your mind, "see" yourself going through the experience successfully and easily.

You may have to keep practicing this for some time, but as you do, get the feeling of safety and trust, which comes from knowing God supports you and will never let you down.

OFF THE MAIN TRAIL

(This activity is only for one who has decided it's time to get rid of his or her worst fear.)

Consider the story of our friend who decided to fly. She took action. What specific step or steps will you take in conquering your fear? What specific affirmation will you use? Start taking your steps and using your affirmation. As you do, in a separate notebook, keep a record of how you are progressing, along with comments about your feelings.

STEPPING-STONE

Act spontaneously.

Be sure that you get prayed up and positive each morning before you begin your day, so that you don't act out of fear based on past experience. Just follow your heart each day this week and act spontaneously throughout the entire day. Don't take time to think of how you acted before, that's just dragging the past into the present. Allow yourself to be fresh.

God is in charge of your life.

Spring is past, summer is gone, and winter is here. And the song that I was meant to sing is still unsung. I have spent my days stringing and restringing my instrument.
—Author unknown

It may be hard to believe that this is the best time of your life, yet it is because it is the *only* time of your life. That is the concept which this Teaching is all about. Nothing else exists except the eternal *now*. God and all good things are present in your life as you read these lines. You can choose to align yourself with God and good, or you can continue to bring the past or the future to this moment. It's like hurrying through a meal to get to the dessert. If you do, you miss all of the nuances of taste that the appetizer and entrée present.

SOUL-TALK

I accept my good now.

1. _____

2. _____

3. _____

SOUL-THOUGHTS

LEAVING THE PAST

The first cars were not called "automobiles" by the public. After so many years of seeing horses pulling carriages, people just couldn't get used to seeing carriages proceeding down the street with nothing pulling them, so they called them "horseless carriages." In fact, so tied was society's consciousness to the past that the designers of these first automobiles installed buggy whip holders, a useless carryover from another era. It wasn't until the consciousness of society changed completely that the last vestiges of the horse-drawn era disappeared.

1. What kind of "buggy whip holders" are you carrying around in your consciousness? In what areas are you "walking backwards" through life? Is an early bankruptcy giving you problems with your present self-worth? Is an early childhood trauma dictating much of your present behavior? To what extent are you using the past as a blueprint for the present? *Identify all of the buggy whip holders that are no longer useful to you.*

2. Looking to the future can be as fruitless as looking to the past. *In what way are your thoughts and feelings about the future affecting your present happiness?* For instance, are you waiting for someone to come into your life or something to occur to make you happy? Is a pervasive fear of the outcome of something in the future ruining your present?

3. *What were your "if onlys" as a child? List as many as you can.* For example, "If only I were bigger, I could stay up later." "If only my parents wouldn't fight so much, I'd be happier."

What were your "if onlys" as a teenager? "If only I were prettier, I'd be more popular."

What were your "if onlys" as a young adult? "If only I had a better job, she might marry me."

What are your "if onlys" now?

4. This moment, as you read these lines, is a brand-new moment in your life. You can choose to be more relaxed, more trusting, more forgiving, more loving. You can choose to be whatever you want. The question is: *Are you treating this moment in a new way? If so, how? If not, why not?*

5. *What are the wonderful possibilities that exist for you in this now moment, at this Possibility Junction? List as many as you can.*

OFF THE MAIN TRAIL

Comment at length on the following statement in the Guidebook: "When you *yearn* for the past, you make yourself a slave to the past. When you *learn* from the past, you become a master of the present."

STEPPING-STONE

Act "as if" today. Choose what you want to be today and act all day as if you really were that way. For example:

"I will act *as if* I were a very patient person."

"I will act *as if* I really enjoy my work."

"I will act *as if* I am prosperous."

"I will act *as if* I love everyone."

Remember, the mind doesn't know the difference between something real and something vividly imagined.

You accept your good now.

CHILD OF GOD

It is a wise child that knows his own father.

—Homer

A TRAGIC MISCONCEPTION

In a desert land of Arabian horses, an orphaned foal was raised by a family of camels. As the young colt grew, he did everything the camels did. He plodded tirelessly across the hot sands. He toted large burdens of cargo on his back, and he watered his parched mouth at every oasis. Once he kicked up his heels in a sudden impulse to run, but then only swayed along at a lumbering pace, because—that's the way camels are supposed to run, aren't they?

After many years of camel life, the Arabian steed grew old and tired. One day, as his weary eyes looked out across a sea of sand, he saw a magnificent horse galloping at full speed like the wind, his shiny mane streaming out from his noble head. "What a beautiful animal!" exclaimed the elderly orphan. "What is it?"

"That's an Arabian horse, fastest and most beautiful of all the animals in our land," answered one of the camels.

"Wouldn't it be wonderful to run like that?" mused the old horse. But he put it out of his mind, and he died thinking he was a camel.

WE BECOME WHAT WE THINK WE ARE

What we believe about ourselves determines our lives. The beautiful Arabian steed could never be more than a "camel" because that is what he thought he was. He took his cues from those around him and believed about himself what they believed about him.

What do we humans believe about ourselves? What do you believe about your own self?

SOUL-TALK

I am God's child.

1. _____

2. _____

3. _____

SOUL-THOUGHTS

A MOST BASIC TEACHING

This Teaching, that we are each a child of God, is the most basic Teaching in virtually all of the great religions. What makes this concept of our being a "child" of a cosmic "Parent" so universal? Probably because on an intuitive level, it just plain feels good! Once we accept the fact that God created us, God then becomes our parent.

1. You have no doubt heard the term *child of God* ever since Sunday school or catechism class. You may have thought of God as a man in the sky at that time, so being a child of that man seemed natural. *With your present concept of God, what exactly does the term* child of God *mean to you now?*

2. *What do you feel is your most obvious and personal inheritance from God?* Perhaps you have a great ability to love or a strong desire to teach or to serve, or you feel you've been given the gift of healing. *What characteristic inherited from your Creator do you feel most strongly?*

3. *Do you feel that you have used this special inheritance fully? If so, in what way? If not, why not, and how can you use it more fully?*

FEELINGS ARE THE BRIDGE

Like so many other concepts in this second half of *The Quest*, the concept of our being children of God is one that is not easily intellectualized. It is impossible to come to terms with it merely by thinking it through. Our intellect can only take us so far. It is our feelings that must be the bridge which takes us to a greater understanding of this concept.

CHILD OF GOD MEDITATION

Our self-esteem is always based on who we *think* we are. All too often we take our cues from those around us who may judge us on how we look or dress, the color of our skin, the amount of money we have, our social position, or our heritage. We interpret their feelings toward us and then apply those feelings to ourselves.

But *true* self-esteem is not based on what others say we are, it is based on who we *really* are. And who and what are we? Each of us really is, purely and simply, a child of God. Knowing who you really are is the ultimate self-image.

During your meditation time this week gently introduce the concept of your being a child of God. Be careful not to bring any old thinking with this phrase. Allow it to be fresh and new. Don't intellectualize it because God as Spirit has not procreated but *created* you. Also into this quiet time take the knowledge that God's wish for you is absolute good and that you are God's creation. Allow these two facts to weave themselves back and forth in the loom of your mind until a tapestry of perfect self-esteem is woven.

I am God's child.

God's wish for me is absolute good.

·OFF THE MAIN TRAIL

How has your interaction or relationship with your parents throughout your life affected your concept of your being a child of God?

For example, if your father were a kind and gentle man, you may have a different feeling about being a child of God than if your father were a violent drunk who abused you. If you were raised by someone other than your parents or if they died when you were a youngster, you may experience a different feeling from the term. *After giving this some thought, write a short essay on the subject. Use extra paper if necessary.*

Listen intently to someone.

Every day seek to listen intently to someone who is talking to you. Let the person feel that you really care about him or her. Extend yourself beyond the normal courteous listening to get into the person's mind. Be genuinely interested in wanting to know about this child of God.

You are God's child.

What you see with your eyes shut is what counts.

—Lame Deer
A Sioux medicine man

"Bob is acting hatefully. I certainly don't approve of what he's doing, but in wanting him out of my life, am I being judgmental or am I using good judgment?"

Judgment or judgmental? For someone on a spiritual path, that is the question. How do we know if or when we are putting ourselves above someone whose actions we find repulsive and obnoxious or downright immoral? After all, we are not perfect, so how can we judge another? Being clear on the difference between the two will help.

No one on a spiritual quest wants to be judgmental of another human being. It presumes a moral high ground that is dangerous territory for a spiritual seeker. So here's a good way to know the difference between being judgmental and using your good judgment: Being *judgmental* is stopping your assessment of people at the appearance level, the superficial level of how they look or act, without going past that to the level of their indwelling Christ. You are using good *judgment* if you can see past people's actions—no matter how repellent you feel they are—to the light of the Christ within them. After doing that, you can make a decision about their actions. Of course. your judgment may lead to your putting those people out of your life until they change their actions, but as long as you do so *and still recognize their indwelling divinity*, it's okay.

The important difference between being judgmental and using your judgment is seeing past the appearances to the Christ within. It's the difference between judgmentally thinking another person is inferior and simply judging a person's actions as being inappropriate for you to be around.

SOUL-TALK

 I use good judgment.

1. _____

2. _____

3. _____

SOUL-THOUGHTS

AN OUTDATED DEFENSE

An important part of our ancient defense mechanism as social creatures was to judge others as dangerous or friendly on the basis of their looks. The more a creature differed from us in looks and sounds and actions, the more dangerous it was and the more it was to be avoided. This applied to the animal world in general, including human beings.

While that may have served us well as an adaptive mechanism 50,000 years ago, it is not applicable nor is it particularly useful now as the world shrinks and we are living closer together and are becoming more of a racial and social mixture.

You probably remember times in your life when people judged you unfairly. Perhaps you were judged by the color of your skin or by your nationality or by your social position. Maybe when you were a teenager, you were judged by the length of your hair. Maybe as an adult, you feel you are judged by the lack of it!

At some time in your life, you have probably made rash judgments about others. After all, it is a natural protective mechanism that has to be unlearned.

1. *What was the worst error of judgment toward another person that you ever made? Discuss the circumstances that led to your decision.*

2. *How did you discover you were wrong about that person? Discuss your feelings when you discovered it.*

3. *What was your single worst error in judgment of a situation? Discuss what led you to make the error.*

4. *What do you feel was the most unfair error that anyone made in judging you? Explain how you felt.*

OFF THE MAIN TRAIL

This may take some digging, but right now it's very likely that you are judging someone or something by appearances. It may be a carryover from the past that you have overlooked until now. It could be your attitude toward a certain dress code or a racial group or a religious organization or a nationality or a political party.

Perhaps it is an incident from the past. It could be you are still harboring enmity toward another person. Having come this far on your spiritual journey, it's unlikely that this judgmental attitude will jump up and bite you, begging to be changed. It's probably too subtle for that, but there's a good chance that something is there.

Carefully comb through your life, your attitudes, and your opinions and try to discover at least one area that has been neglected and to which you can now bring your good judgment. Describe your thoughts and feelings about it.

STEPPING-STONE

 Do something every day that needs to be done but that you have been putting off doing. Dedicate the energy you use doing these tasks to a friend or to the members of your Quest group.

What can you do? How about cleaning out the garage or straightening out that closet or fixing that bad step on the back porch? What about that note you have been meaning to write? Whatever you choose to do each day, do it joyously and dedicate it to a friend.

You use good judgment.

*The real baptism is the baptism of the Holy Spirit. No
person or group of persons can give this spiritual
baptism, it is a matter between the individual soul
and the divine source of all light and life and power
and love. When the individual is baptised by the Holy
Spirit, that individual knows it.*

—Myrtle Fillmore

Things of the Spirit can only be discerned by the spirit. The concept of Spirit cannot be understood intellectually. This Teaching, therefore, is not so much to be studied as to be embraced, not so much to be practiced as to be experienced.

SOUL-TALK

I am open to Spirit.

1. _____

2. _____

3. _____

KNOWING BY EXPERIENCING

There are some things in life that cannot be taught, nor can they be learned: an appreciation of a beautiful sunset, the feeling of seeing your firstborn child, the wonder of even a fleeting awareness of your indwelling Christ essence. There can be no teaching or learning involved with such highly personal events. Likewise, there are no activities which can teach you what Spirit is.

God is more than all that is, so Spirit is unknowable. However, just because It cannot be defined doesn't mean It cannot be experienced. It can, and you can experience It by becoming quiet and centered and allowing Spirit to flow through you unrestrained and uninhibited.

1. Other than your *Soul-Talk*, *Soul-Thoughts*, and *Stepping-Stone*, this Spirit Meditation will be the only activity for this Adventure. With this activity there is no writing or reading involved, only "allowing"—allowing the mighty current of Spirit to become one with your spirit and, in doing so, to experience Spirit as the love and peace and joy and inspiration and all good things that It is.

Spirit Meditation

Experience Spirit as it flows through you by becoming quiet and still and centered. Before beginning, take some time to quiet your body and your mind.

Begin your Spirit Meditation by saying the phrase "God is Spirit" *as you exhale. On the next exhale, say* "I am spirit." *Alternate these phrases aloud and with energy. As you say them, one after another, feel the relationship between the two:* "God is Spirit, I am spirit."

Ever so slowly, begin saying these phrases, "God is Spirit, I am spirit," *more and more quietly until they become a mere whisper. Repeat them as a whisper for a while until it feels good to internalize the phrases. But now, with the phrases inside of you, silently affirm* God is Spirit *as you* inhale *while you continue to affirm* I am spirit *as you* exhale. *You are now breathing in* God is Spirit *and breathing out* I am spirit.

Continue this process for a good while until you sense the connectedness.

When you feel it is time to conclude, take a few minutes to sit quietly and allow the process to be completed.

SUMMARY OF SPIRIT MEDITATION

1. Become quiet and still.

2. Begin saying aloud on alternate exhalations: *"God is Spirit,"* then *"I am spirit."*

3. Say these phrases more and more softly until you finally internalize them.

4. When internalized, silently say *"God is Spirit"* when you inhale and *"I am spirit"* when you exhale.

5. Inhale *God is Spirit*, exhale *I am spirit*.

6. Continue until you feel it is time to conclude.

This meditation, then, becomes a perfect metaphor for how Spirit works through you, inspiring you and outworking through you when you allow It.

Also, it hints at the relationship between the Spirit of God and your spirit—separate but joined.

Do your Spirit Meditation at least twice each day this week.

STEPPING-STONE

 Pray for a different friend each day.

Choose a different friend to pray for each day. Include the person in your thoughts and prayers throughout the day. Know that the two of you are connected in spirit.

You are open to Spirit.

THE JESUS CHRIST PRESENCE

Jesus ... is in constant contact with those who raise their thoughts to Him in prayer.
> —Charles Fillmore

What does it mean to have Jesus as your personal Savior? What it does *not* mean is worshiping Jesus the man or putting Him so high on a pedestal that you feel you'll never get there yourself. Jesus discovered and expressed the Christ, the innate divinity of humankind. Because this is the greatest revelation in the history of the world, it is easy to get caught up emotionally in the personality cult built up around Jesus.

Taking Jesus as your personal Savior is more than that. It may begin as an emotional decision based on the personality of Jesus, but unless it transcends His personality and becomes a spiritual experience, it will not contribute to your spiritual growth.

A MYSTICAL EMBRACE

A decision for Jesus is not a blind embrace of a

man who was so obviously a spiritual skyscraper. It is a mystical embrace of a fellow traveler on the quest who went before us and is helping us on our way.

Yes, indeed, we can feel the presence of Jesus Christ and we can claim Him for our personal Savior. The reason it seems so natural is because He is so at one with God that we can't tell where one begins and the other ends. His presence is God presence yet He was like us, a flesh-and-blood human being, and we can so much more easily identify with a flesh-and-blood man than with the pure Spirit of God.

SOUL-TALK

I am one with Jesus Christ.

1. _____

2. _____

3. _____

SOUL-THOUGHTS

The closer you feel to Jesus the man, the more you will be able to experience Jesus the Christ *if you stay open to it.* The danger is that it's very easy to let the emotions engendered by His personality stand in the way of the more mystical experience of His presence.

1. Have you ever had a picture of an admired person prominently displayed? Maybe when you were a teenager, for instance, you had a poster of a movie star or a sports figure on your wall? Possibly now you have a picture of a departed loved one on your desk. *Consider your feeling of oneness with that person. Why do or did you have his or her picture? What does or did seeing the picture do for you? Discuss this at length.*

2. *Who is the most Jesus Christlike person you know?*

Analyze why this person is more like Jesus Christ than anyone else you know.

3. *If you are comfortable with the idea of a personal relationship with Jesus Christ, in what ways would you like to experience His presence?*

4. When Jesus was about to leave His disciples at the end of His ministry, He reminded them that in all of their time together, they had never asked Him for anything. He then proceeded to tell them to ask of Him, that He might lovingly answer their needs. *With what part or parts of your life would you want Jesus' help? What would you like Him to do for you?*

5. *At least once a day during this week, take time to do either of these special meditations to help you to identify more closely with Jesus Christ.* Read them both to determine which one most appeals to you. By faithfully using one or the other (or both!) in time, the Jesus Christ presence will reveal Itself to you.

Jesus Christ Meditation #1

Just as surely as you can "feel" the presence of a departed loved one, you can feel the presence of Jesus Christ. It is always available, but like the stations available to a radio, we must "tune in" the Jesus Christ presence. We can do that by becoming quiet and still and asking Jesus to come into our lives.

When you are ready to experience the Jesus Christ presence, sit quietly and open your mind and heart to the reality of His presence, not only around *you but in you and affirm aloud:* Jesus, I am open and receptive. Make Your presence known to me. *Let that thought sit for five or six breaths and then repeat aloud:* Jesus, I am open and receptive. Make Your presence known to me. *Let it sit again for five or six breaths and then repeat it once again.* Jesus, I am open and receptive. Make Your presence known to me. *Allow the thought to settle in comfortably.*

Then affirm silently: Jesus, I feel Your presence. *Feel your consciousness expand as you become the open channel that allows His presence to make Itself known to you.*

Feel your oneness with Jesus Christ. Feel His presence around you and as part of you. More than anything, feel His consciousness. Feel His love. You and He are one. Rest in that knowledge.

Jesus Christ Meditation #2

Seek a quiet spot, relax your body and still your mind. With your great power of imagination, lead yourself back about two thousand years to Judea. See Jesus the man in the Judean hills preaching and teaching. See the crowds around Him. Observe the scene in detail—the time of day, the landscape, the faces in the crowd. Observe Jesus. How is He dressed? See His shoes and His clothes. Identify the color of His hair and eyes. Follow Him as a part of the crowd. Get a feel for the type of person Jesus was. Take your time noting as many details as you can.

Then, with the swiftness of your imagination, shift the scene to that night. You are sitting around Jesus' campfire with the disciples when Jesus comes and sits next to you. He looks directly into your eyes and you look into His. In your mind, dialogue with Him. Ask Him whatever questions you wish to and hear His answers. Continue as long as the conversation lasts. When the scene dissolves, sit quietly and allow yourself ample time to ruminate and reflect on Jesus and on your meditation.

OFF THE MAIN TRAIL

Consider this quote from John 3:16:

"For God so loved the world that he gave his only Son, that whoever believes in him should not perish but have eternal life."

Is this quote compatible with the assertion that it is not mandatory that we take Jesus Christ as our personal Savior? Explain your answer.

Ask yourself, "What would I do if I were Jesus?" Then do it.

Before making any decision this week, ask yourself, "What would I do if I were Jesus?" When you have determined what He would do, go ahead and do it. Let your entire decision-making process be centered on what Jesus would do in any situation. Certainly there are other considerations in any decision—money, time, availability, relationships, and so much more. No decision is made without considering all of the almost infinite amount of variables involved.

This week, however, put yourself in the position of Jesus and let all decisions—personal, business, financial, social, and any others, begin with the question, What would I do if I were Jesus?

You are one with Jesus Christ.

RELATIONSHIPS

Love does not consist in gazing at each other but in looking outward together in the same direction.
    —Antoine de Saint-Exupéry

Next time you're in a bookstore, take a look at the "Self-Help" section. You'll see an abundance of books on relationships: *How to Get Along With Your Boss ... Your Neighbor ... Your Kids ... Your Parents ...* and so on.

You are probably also aware of courses which are offered to teach you how to get the most from your employees, or how to take charge of a relationship.

In short, how to get along with others is big business! We're told how to identify certain types of people—the aggressive, the passive, the procrastinator, the easily motivated, and others. Then we're given detailed instructions on how to treat these people, how to act, what to say, and when to say it. The implicit message is that if we identify people correctly and treat them in accordance with the rules for these types of people, we will be able to get along with them.

Yet relationships are more than emotion-to-emotion contact. That's much too superficial. Trying to understand a relationship or to effect a change in that relationship from the psychological level alone is like trying to care for wildflowers by identifying each individual flower and then giving separate attention to each petal and stem.

A relationship, at its worst, is seeing the differences in each other. At its best, it is a touching of souls, a seeing of the Christ in each other. Rather than treating stems and petals, treating a relationship on a Christ-to-Christ basis is like watering the roots of the wildflowers.

NO TECHNIQUES NEEDED

When you can see yourself as part of God and then see the other person as part of God, you will see him or her as part of you! Then you will *automatically* think, do, and say the right thing. There are no tricks needed, no techniques to memorize and apply. In fact, such superficial systems just get in the way of a deeper relationship. A Christ-to-Christ connection puts the relationship on a love basis, and love speaks a language that all can understand.

SOUL-TALK

The Christ in me sees the Christ in others.

1. _____

2. _____

3. _____

SOUL-THOUGHTS

THE "HUMAN" TRAP

When we operate only from our humanness, we can easily fall into the old habit of recognizing differences. In our physical evolution, this tendency to avoid anything unlike us served us well. It enabled us to avoid those creatures that were different from us, which were often predators.

This atavistic trait no longer serves us well in our spiritual evolution. In concentrating on our differences, we often overlook our sameness. Thus, color of skin may take on disproportional importance, as may a person's sex. Nationality and religious preference may be accorded a distorted significance. In regarding these superficial differences as important, we may assume that changing those differences or at least coming to terms with them will change the relationship.

However, changing the surface can never change the core. An apple seed does not change because the apple is peeled. "First within, then without." Relationships *begin* inside of us and color our world. So relationships are never "mended." If they are to be changed, they must be taken to another plateau.

1. *List the names of five friends. Then list five people you are having trouble getting along with.*

Friends:

Others:

2. *Write out some* positive *emotional and spiritual traits that you have discerned in each of these people.*

For example:

Friends:

 Joe—Always happy.
  Considerate of others.
 Mary—Talks lovingly about her children.
  Takes time to listen to people's problems.

Others:

 Steve—Seems to be nice to his mother.
  Will sometimes laugh at a good joke.

3. *Discuss any positive emotional or spiritual traits that overlap between your friends and those you don't get along with.*

For example: "Jim, whom I don't get along with, and my friend Bob both collect for XYZ charity. I think that is a worthwhile thing to do."

4. *What were the first things you liked about your best friends? What drew you to them?*

5. What were the first things you did not like about the "others"?

A NOT-SO-HIDDEN MESSAGE

When we feel people are cruel to us or treat us unfairly, their words and actions are a signal to us that they need love. Every frown is a sign that translates into: "*Attention! Love needed!*" Every cross word is a signal: "*I am desperate. I badly need your love!*" We can't know that person's mind or know what's hidden in the recesses of the soul, but we can know one thing: This person is not unhappy because of what has been done to him or her as traumatic or sad as that might be. This individual is unhappy because love is not expressing through him or her. Every angry person has a problem with being able to fully express love.

6. *Select one of the people from your list of "others" and at your earliest opportunity establish a Christ-to-Christ rapport. Make the experience brief, a few moments will be enough. As you look directly into this person's eyes, speak a sentence or two which arises from your Christ self. Then later, write down your comments, your feelings, about the experience.*

OFF THE MAIN TRAIL

List the specific *steps you can take to help the ten people you listed express love more fully.*

Be as specific as possible. It does no good to deal in generalities when addressing specific situations.

What can you do to help each person to express more love? Give it much thought. Make a plan. Be creative.

After you have listed the steps, follow through on them.

STEPPING-STONE

Do not be judgmental of anyone for one full week.

You'll have plenty of opportunity, you can be sure of that! Many times throughout the day, people will present you with the occasion to judge them and their actions. From the person who cuts your car off on the expressway, to the one who jumps in front of you in the supermarket line, to a loved one who shows you flaming anger—each time incidents like these present themselves, you will have to make a decision. You can assess their actions as bad, presume that they are wrong for doing it, take it personally, and respond in kind. This is being judgmental.

Or you can use your judgment and see that not-so-invisible sign around that person's neck which reads: *"Please, love me."*

The Christ in you sees the Christ in others.

$\mathcal{H}$ELPING OTHERS

Help your brother's boat across, and your own will reach the shore.
　　　　　　　　　　　—Hindu Proverb

How many people in your life need help? If you carefully consider this question, your answer will probably be "all of them!" And it's true.

Even the highly evolved spiritual leaders that we respect pray for help: more tolerance, more love, more understanding, more knowledge of God. Virtually all of us feel incomplete at some level, but as we've already noted in *The Quest*, any need, any feeling of lack, any incompleteness can always be traced to a disconnection with our Christ nature. There is no human activity which alone can make us feel reconnected.

Those we love whom we want to help do indeed need us, but it's not the human of us that they need. It is the Christ of us. They have lost sight of their divinity and we, if we identify them with their problem, have lost sight of theirs *and* ours. They need us, not to help them manipulate the ever-changing circumstances of their lives, but rather to focus on their unchanging core. The best way to help them is to see the Christ in them and to let them see you seeing the Christ in them so that they will follow your gaze!

NO HELP AT ALL?

This is a good time to make clear that seeing the Christ in someone does not preclude working from the human level too. For example, speaking to your boss about a job for your friend who is out of work may help him or her get work. Driving your aunt to the hospital so that she can get her radiation treatment is a kind and generous thing to do and will assist in her healing. Calling or writing a letter to a co-worker who is in a deep depression has a healing quality and would be most welcome.

But *any human help must always be anchored in a firm belief in underlying wholeness.* To act *only* from our human side is to assume that we know what is best for someone else.

How often have we acted strictly from our human side and gotten ourselves into trouble? What makes us think that the human of us is any better at sorting things out for others than it is for ourselves? We know that to effect meaningful changes in our lives, we must pray for guidance, listen to that guidance, and then follow that guidance. Yet for others, we often barge right into their lives, "knowing" what is best for them.

Helping others, no matter what other steps are taken, can only be effective when we see these people whole and complete.

SOUL-TALK

 I let my Christ light shine.

1. _____

2. _____

3. _____

SOUL-THOUGHTS

 1. *Name the three closest people in your life who you feel need help. After each name, list what specific help is needed.*

For example:

Joe—needs a job

Mary—healing of lungs

Bob—lifting of a depression

2. *Now list exactly what human steps you can take to effect a change in that person. Be thorough.*

For example: "I can help my friend with his job application. I can help him rewrite his résumé. I can encourage him with phone calls every day."

3. Do you believe that if you were to follow all of the steps you wrote for these people and if they were to do all of the things you listed, that they would be over their present problem forever? Explain your answer.

4. After each name listed, write a short paragraph on what specific thoughts you can hold that are most conducive to helping that person.

OFF THE MAIN TRAIL

For each of the three people named in Activity 1, make up a suitable prayer acknowledging the Christ in that person and affirming the good that you see for him or her through this present challenge.

For example: "Joe, divine order is established in your life. You surrender to the Christ within you, and you are led to the perfect job."

Call forth an image of each person and read their prayers at least one time each day this week.

STEPPING-STONE

Participate in the spiritual growth of others.

There are lots of ways you can do this. Consciously realize that every person you meet and every person you think about is divine. Don't fall into any old habits of prejudgment. Be *consciously* aware that every person you meet or think about has the divine potential in him or her. "See" the indwelling Christ and pray for his or her perfect good. Be aware of your thinking when you are with others, and if you are thinking about a person or reacting to a person in a negative way, change your thinking to one of love and support. Make a spiritual connection with everyone this week.

In addition, pray for the good of all people, everywhere. Share spiritual literature with others *(but only those who are receptive to it).* Contribute your time and your finances to the spiritual movement with which you feel the closest rapport and which you feel is doing positive work.

You let your Christ light shine.

THANKSGIVING

Who does not thank for little will not thank for much.

—Estonian Proverb

"Fake it until you make it" may sound like the wrong approach when sincerely trying to turn your life around. Yet it's not really bad advice. When we "fake it," when we force ourselves to consistently think in a certain way and consistently "pretend" we are feeling certain emotions, our minds will eventually begin to accept those thoughts. By consciously acting "as if," we are creating new neural pathways, new ways for the brain to think. This can then change our feelings and behavior, which of course means we are changing our lives.

If, for example, we were to consciously think in a loving rather than spiteful way of someone we resent, over time our hard feelings would eventually soften and be replaced by feelings of love. If we "fake" feelings of love with enough willingness and consistency, in time we really will love. The innate divine love that had been suppressed is then given permission to express itself.

This technique works especially well with thanksgiving, because our words represent our feelings. Words of thanksgiving, whether faked or real, represent feelings of gratitude, trust, and faith. They represent feelings that everything will be all right, and they open us up to receive the good already waiting for us.

SOUL-TALK

Thank You, God.

1. _____

2. _____

3. _____

SOUL-THOUGHTS

When we give thanks, we are really giving our blessing. Like sunflowers turning toward the sun, giving thanks turns our hearts toward our good.

We know the power of thanksgiving on a human, emotional plane. We all like to be appreciated and thanked. It motivates us and opens us up to do better.

On a spiritual plane, when we are sincerely thankful to God for the good we have and the good in store for us, thanksgiving takes on an even more attracting power. Like a powerful magnet, thanksgiving attracts our good to us.

1. The obvious tactic is to ask you to list the things for which you are thankful. We won't disappoint you! *On separate index cards, write out seven things that you are thankful for—one to a card.*

For example: I thank You, God, for my health.

2. *On seven other index cards, write out seven separate things for which you would like to be thankful. (Be sure to write them out as if they were already true.)*

For example: If you would like to be thankful for a better relationship with your mate, write out: "I thank You, God, for a wonderful marriage."

If you want to be thankful for increased prosperity, you might write: "I thank You, God, that all my needs are met."

3. *Every day this week, take a card from each group (Activity 1 and 2) and repeat your statements as many times during the day as you think about it.*

4. *Each day this week take some time to sit quietly and connect with the feelings of thanksgiving deep*

within you. Lead into your quiet time by whispering, "Thank You, God" several times. When you are finished with these moments of stillness, say aloud "Thank You, God."

OFF THE MAIN TRAIL

The biblical story of loaves and fishes is a classic story of the power of thanksgiving. You will recall that there were many thousands of people to be fed and only a few loaves and fishes with which to feed them. Jesus, however, did not look at what He did *not* have. He gave thanks for what He *did* have, and in giving thanks was able to attain His good.

Read Matthew 15:29-39. What is your explanation for what took place? What is the significance of Jesus' giving thanks?

STEPPING-STONE

Believe that everyone you come in contact with loves you.

Whether it's the clerk at the hardware store, the toll collector, a new client, or a traveling salesman, believe that each person you come in contact with loves you. When you are about to meet someone or to come in contact with someone, believe in advance that this person loves you.

Believing that everyone loves you is not as far-fetched as it may seem because, on a Christ-to-Christ level, they do! They and you and we—all of us—are part of the one Force that is God; therefore, on that level, it is impossible for us not to love each other. We *are* each other!

The funny thing about it is that if you believe people love you, you will love them more. Not only that, when you love them more, they will love you more. It's a self-fulfilling act.

Thank You, God.

𝒫ROSPERITY

If you will do what is yours to do and be what is yours to be, life will provide you the means to do it and be it.

—James Dillet Freeman

It is difficult to think lofty thoughts when your body is in pain or you are distracted by your stomach growling, and it's difficult to think of your spiritual life when you are worrying about your rent. It is only when your physical needs are satisfied that you can best turn your attention to your spiritual path. Prosperity, having your needs met, allows you to take the next step in your spiritual development.

SOUL-TALK

I accept my prosperity.

1. _____

2. _____

3. _____

SOUL-THOUGHTS

Note: In this final quarter of *The Quest,* continue to take enough time writing your *Soul-Thoughts.* Allow the reflections in the higher levels of your consciousness to speak to you. Be open to new insights and scrupulously note them in your *Soul-Thoughts* section. Your *Soul-Thoughts* are the journal of your unfolding soul. It is your unconsciousness that is speaking to you. Honor it by noting everything that it has to say.

You know by now that what you think about, what you put your attention on, grows. Thinking of lack is as powerful an image as thinking of abundance.

1. *What needs do you want fulfilled? Make a list of those things that you feel would allow you to pursue the spiritual path with greater ease.*

Perhaps you spend lots of time worrying about making ends meet and feel that a better-paying job would address this need.

DON'T WANT IT? DON'T SAY IT

Don't give the energy of your thoughts and emotions and especially your words to something you don't want in your life. Instead, create a prosperity vocabulary. Speak only words of prosperity and abundance. Express only words of thanksgiving and praise and blessing.

Words exert an enormous power, as you have learned in other Teachings, and so you will want to use them with deliberate intent. Be aware of the words you use, and if they are not saying what you want in your life, then change them at once. In other words, *if you don't want it, don't say it.*

2. *Take an inventory of your words regarding prosperity. What words or phrases do you regularly use that conflict with what you feel you need?*

For example: Do you often say, "That's too expensive for me"? It may take you a few days to catch yourself saying things you don't mean but, each time you do, make a note to change it.

3. *How can you change the words you have been using to better mirror the truth about your prosperity, which is that God's will for you is good?*

4. When you think about your prosperity, there are certain thoughts and emotions that automatically come to mind. It's important that these feelings be examined.

How do you "see" yourself now? Do you see yourself as someone who is prosperous and creative? Do you see yourself as someone who deserves prosperity? Spend some quiet time examining these questions. What are the feelings that come up when you think about them? When you can identify them, list these feelings and write about them as extensively as you can.

5. *What specific steps can you take to begin to cultivate thoughts and feelings of prosperity and creativity?*

A good technique for increasing prosperity is imaging. Rather than imaging wealth, however, it's infinitely more effective to image yourself as an open channel to the abundant flow of creative ideas that will lead to having all your needs met.

SUPPORTING YOUR SOURCE

Are you actively supporting the source of your spiritual nourishment?

The most important component of prosperity is giving. The flow of God's good must be kept moving. As you move it out to do more of God's work, more will be given to you. (We know a very renowned businessman who now tithes about 50 percent of his earnings and says he cannot stop the increasing flow of prosperity into his life.)

Are you taking a portion of your good and distributing it to your source of spiritual inspiration and nourishment? (Giving to charitable organizations is fine, but should not be regarded as a tithe or as part of your "giving back to God.")

6. *Make a list of all the areas from which you receive spiritual inspiration.* Include all churches, publications, people, seminars, and so forth.

In what way are you now supporting them? Are you supporting them with your money? Your time? Your prayers?

If you are not now supporting them, what specific plans do you have to do so?

OFF THE MAIN TRAIL

In the biblical story of the Israelites wandering in the desert (Exodus 16, Numbers 11), manna fell from the sky every night. This "daily bread" was sufficient for each day and would again appear in a sufficient amount the next day.

What is your metaphysical interpretation of this story? What lessons about prosperity does it point out to you?

STEPPING-STONE

 Bless your bills as you receive them, as you write your checks, and as you mail the payments.

Sound difficult to do? It's not. Actually, it gets easier and easier and eventually becomes a great joy.

Those bills represent services rendered, prosperity given to you. By paying them, you are just passing on a service, in the form of money, to someone else. Like the manna sent down from God, more will be given to you as you need it. Blessing the bills is really giving thanksgiving for your abundance—the abundance you have now and the abundance that you will have in the future.

You accept your prosperity.

*T*HE PHYSICAL WORLD

Our body is a fragment of the cosmos,
arranged in a very special way, but
obeying the same laws as the rest of
the world.

> —Alexis Carrel

The physical laws that we are aware of operate in a space/time continuum. Some of them may seem to conflict with what we often refer to as "spiritual laws," but actually there is no conflict. The only place a conflict may exist is in our incomplete understanding of the world and the laws which govern it.

The space/time physical world is part of our spiritual existence. The creative process does not divide itself into physical, mental, and spiritual. There is only a separation in our understanding of our universe and of parts of ourselves.

In fact, there is a far higher Intelligence and Power existing than our human senses can perceive. We are dependent on It for our physical existence. It is the Source of all that we are, of our very identity.

SOUL-TALK

I am part of God, and God is part of me.

1. _____

2. _____

3. _____

SOUL-THOUGHTS

    1. *How have you, in the past, "put God to a foolish test"? Describe some examples.*

    You may have prayed for a safe trip and driven at excessive speeds. Perhaps you prayed for weight loss but regularly ate rich desserts.

2. *Identify any present actions in your life that you feel are not consistent with God's laws as you know them.*

Asking God for help with a healing but refusing to follow your doctor's suggestions is an example.

3. *Make a list of phenomena that are as yet unexplainable by you but that you feel have a logical explanation.*

These could include hands-on healings you may have witnessed or "knowing" someone was going to call you, only to have the phone ring and it be that person.

OFF THE MAIN TRAIL

Check out your diet. Analyze your current eating habits for inconsistencies in what your desires are for wholeness and what you are eating. Are the foods you eat consistent with the rules of nutrition as you know them? Is everything that you put into your mouth something that you feel is good for you? If not, what statement is this making to your subconscious about your health? Comment on each inconsistency.

*Also, pay close attention to the foods you eat.
Make a conscious effort to put into your body temple
only those foods that you sincerely feel are worthy of
becoming your tissues. It's great to give a blessing
before a meal, but this week bless the food as you make
up your shopping list, as you purchase the food, as you
prepare it, and as you eat it.*

STEPPING-STONE

Listen to beautiful music every day.

From the time you wake up until the time you get
to work, listen to beautiful music. If you regularly
listen to or watch the news, don't follow that schedule
this week. Instead, find a station that plays something
beautiful or listen to music of your own. Start the
music as soon as you awaken and keep it on until you
leave the house for work. Continue it on your car
radio until you get to work. If you stay at home and do
not go out to work, it may be much easier for you to
listen to beautiful music throughout the day. If you
feel you are already listening to beautiful music, then
this week listen to a different style of beautiful music.

You are part of God, and God is part of you.

Be careful about reading health books.
You may die of a misprint.
                    —Mark Twain

Psychosomatic illness is illness caused by thoughts. It is a well-documented phenomenon, and no serious student of medicine or psychology doubts its existence.

Yet, if we can believe in psychosomatic illness, the ability of the mind to make a healthy body sick, can't we believe in psychosomatic health? It is just a small step in another direction to believe that if the mind can break down a body that is healthy, then the mind can build up a body that is sick.

That's not where it ends. Sure, we can do a lot on our own to become well. We can eat good foods, exercise, follow the suggestions of our doctors, and more. But what about the next step, that step past body and mind into spirit, past wellness into wholeness? When we are centered in our spirit, we then experience *all* of the gifts that God gave us. It is our Father's good pleasure to give us the kingdom. It is only when we put God at the beginning and end of the equation that we can become whole.

SOUL-TALK

I am whole.

1. _____

2. _____

3. _____

SOUL-THOUGHTS

ALWAYS NEW

The Guidebook stated that we are always replacing the atoms of our bodies. In fact, in less than one year's time, we will have replaced almost 100 percent of our atoms! The brain cells which did our thinking last year will not be the same ones we have now. Our livers will be different than our livers of two months ago. These new atoms will give us new bones in about three months and a new covering of skin in about one month. Our stomach linings will be new in less than a week from now. Even the DNA which is responsible for our shapes, our sizes, the color of our hair and eyes, in fact the most minute detail of our physical bodies, was not the same DNA even two months ago!

Yet with all of this newness, why do the patterns remain?

TWO CHANGES NEEDED

If we want to change the pattern of health in our own physical bodies, there are two factors with which we must deal. The first is the collective ideas of the entire human race (often called race consciousness), which are mostly negative and expectant of disease and death. The second is our own personal ideas, which are also apt to parallel race consciousness and be negative and expectant of illness and demise.

So our first task is to refuse to be affected by others' beliefs, and then to adjust our own beliefs as well. A big order? Yes, but not so big that it can't be done. God is a *living* God, ever on the side of life. It is God who empowers the life-force in each cell of our bodies. We have the support of the entire cosmos in our movement toward wholeness.

316

SPEAKING AND LISTENING

Two of the most powerful transformational tools that we have are the power of our spoken words and the power inherent in the silence.

Our spoken word is our claim upon the universal substance. It is what we are asking for, what we want. It is how we think and relate to our universe, including our own bodies.

The silence is where and how we connect with God. It is where we "listen" to what God has to "say." It is the space beyond time and space, where we simply "are." This is the level on which new patterns are created and emerge. It is a level beyond thought, where we simply "know."

Reread the Mile Markers in Teaching 12, "The Silence," and Teaching 20, "The Power of the Spoken Word."

BODY-BLESSING

Everyone likes to be complimented. Everyone works a little harder, does a little better, when he or she is complimented for doing a good job.

Fear can force us to do better, but improvements last only as long as we are fearful. Love, on the other hand, inspires us to do better. The glow of feeling loved and appreciated lingers long past fear's motivating emotion.

Your body has a need to feel loved. Regularly blessing your organs, tissues, and cells "motivates" them to perform as they were created to perform and as they were designed to perform. Your body loves to hear the truth about itself. It breaks whatever pattern

317

it was following to follow a new design.

BLESS YOUR BODY

Take time to bless your body. Do it on a regular basis as part of a meditative experience. However, it can also be done whenever you have a few minutes, even at a traffic light or waiting for an appointment or during a television commercial.

The following is a suggestion for a more formal experience of body-blessing. Make an effort to do this regularly. This will be the only other activity in this Adventure.

Body-Blessing Meditation

Prepare yourself for your special Body-Blessing Meditation by sitting in your normal meditation spot and becoming quiet.

When you feel you are still and centered, begin talking to your body, either silently or aloud. Bring to mind each organ and thank it for helping to bring you life, and then give it your blessing. "Thank you, heart, for pumping my blood. I love you and I bless you." Do this until you have thanked and blessed each of the organs of your body.

(Don't spend extra time on a part of the body that has been giving you trouble. Thank it and bless it just as you would thank and bless any other organ or tissue or muscle.)

When you are finished blessing, empty your mind of all conscious thoughts. Do not try to recap any feelings you had during your blessings. As thoughts bubble up, allow them to drift by. Do not entertain any of them but gently allow them to leave your conscious thinking. Bask in the silence. If God "speaks" to you in this

318

silence, don't analyze, just listen.

(If you are having trouble with too many thoughts, take an affirmation into the silence with you. An appropriate one for this Body-Blessing Meditation would be something like, "Thank You, God.")

When you feel that it is time to stop your meditation, gently bring your attention back to your room.

End your Body-Blessing Meditation with the words, "Thank You, God, for Your life-force within me."

STEPPING-STONE

Forgive yourself for something.

Get rid of any unforgiveness that you have been directing toward yourself. Get rid of it this week!

For example, forgive yourself for breaking your promise to yourself to stop smoking or to lose weight or to begin night school. Forgive yourself for judging others or hurting others or for hurting someone who is now dead. Forgive yourself for holding negative thoughts about yourself or for doing something stupid or for getting angry at your children. You are not the person you were last year or last week or yesterday or when you began to read this paragraph. Forgiving yourself will remind you that you are as new as your last thought.

You are whole.

CONTINUITY OF LIFE

The road of life winds on, and we like travelers go
From turn to turn until we come to know
The truth that life is endless and that we
Forever are inhabitants of all eternity.
                              —Martha Smock

While our scientists have yet to prove conclusively that we exist before and after this earthly experience, we know that as a part of God, we cannot have a beginning and an end. Our essential identity has always been and always will be.

What is a provable fact is that God has given us the gift of life now and that within us is a life-force that knows only life. It is incumbent upon us to do the very best we can to allow that life-force to express utterly and completely. This includes affirming as often as possible in our words and actions what it is that we sense, that the essential core of us is immortal.

SOUL-TALK

 I live forever.

1. _____

2. _____

3. _____

SOUL-THOUGHTS

LIFE INCLUDES DEATH

Fear of death is the fear that drives virtually all other fears and, of course, we cannot live life to the fullest if we fear death. Life is for living, not for fearing, and we will never find the knowledge of life by looking only at death. Our immortal spirit is inextricably found in the study of life.

Yet, life does include death; it must. Life goes through stages, and each is in reality a death. The

321

infant dies to the child. The child dies to the youth. The youth dies to the adult. You have died many "deaths," and you will die many more as you continue to identify yourself on higher and higher levels of life.

The one constant in all of these changes is that all of the changes you have made have been observed by you. It is that very self of you which has been doing the observing that does not die. In fact, it is that self which seeks greater and greater expression of life— each new expression causing the "death" of the former expression. How better to let go of limitations? As each limitation is discarded, a new expression of the real you is born. Yet whether you are expressing as the infant or the child or the youth or the adult, you have remained you! You never lost your identity, you merely put on a different expression of that core essence that is you.

You cannot die in the sense that you can cease to be. God's plan for you is life—eternal life—body, mind, and spirit functioning harmoniously as one. Any plan that fails to fulfill this is doomed to die and to be born again and again and again until the plan is fulfilled.

1. *List as many of your "deaths" and subsequent rebirths as you can think of.*

Graduating from high school, reaching teen years, becoming of legal age, going on your first date, perhaps even beginning *The Quest*—these are some examples you might list.

322

2. *What was the most meaningful "death" and rebirth? Include the details and discuss why it was the most meaningful.*

You could discuss the day you got married or had a child or were involved in a divorce.

3. *What do you feel will be your next important "death," and what rebirth do you think it will lead to?*

4. The following meditation and written exercise should be done every day that you spend on this Adventure.

MEDITATION ON LIFE

Reread the section in this Adventure titled "Life Includes Death" before each regular meditation time this week. Allow your unconscious to tell you about life and birth and death and God. Allow the life-force within each cell of your body to speak to you.

When you have finished your meditation, write down all of the feelings and impressions that you can put into words. Please use your separate notebook on this one.

TIME IS NOT TOXIC

One of the most serious inhibitors to life in our society is our preoccupation with death, and a subtle way we refer to death is the morbid attention our society gives to age. Rather than counting each decade as a milestone, we treat it as a millstone that drags us closer to death.

One can't read a newspaper or magazine without reading someone's name followed by his or her age. To dwell on age is to limit the life-force in its expression of life. A year is but a revolution of the earth around the sun. To feel that fifty or sixty or seventy revolutions around the sun can somehow affect the life-force within us is to limit it. Time is not toxic. Time is chronological, not pathological. The movement of the hands of a clock can do us no harm, but our dwelling on age can. Dwelling on death limits life.

OFF THE MAIN TRAIL

From this point on, pay no attention to age, yours or anyone else's. Allow the life-force within you to express without the inhibition of yours or society's negative thoughts concerning the number of times you or someone else has circled the sun. The truth is that your age is really none of your business. It is a meaningless number and should not have the least bit of control of your life.

STEPPING-STONE

Don't talk about yourself.

Chances are really good that if someone did not specifically ask, he or she is not really interested in how your life is going. Ask yourself, honestly, is there any reason that this person would be interested? If you are with someone and are not talking about yourself, you will probably be listening to the other person. If you are, then give this person the best "listen" he or she has ever had.

You live forever.

Without humility there can be no humanity.
—John Buchan

Let's talk for a minute about metal. Think of silver. Why is it the best conductor of electricity? Why can more electricity flow through it than any other metal? The reason: Of all the metals, silver is the least resistant to the flow of electricity and because of this, silver yields the least heat and the least waste while allowing the highest voltage.

Now think of iron. Iron can conduct electricity, but it is highly resistant to the flow and therefore yields lower voltages. Iron is so resistant, in fact, that most of the energy is wasted as heat. Very little is channeled through the iron itself to emerge as usable energy.

Why this talk about the conductivity of metals? Because it teaches us a major lesson: *allow!* Get yourself so far out of the way that the activity of Spirit can

work unimpeded in your life. How? Not by resisting,
but by humbly accepting the presence of God working
through you.

SOUL-TALK

*It is not I but the Christ within which does the
work.*

1. _____

2. _____

3. _____

SOUL-THOUGHTS

AUTHENTICITY THE KEY

The key to humility is authenticity. We are less than authentic when we believe that who and what we are are less than sufficient for the circumstances we are presented with, that we must somehow supplement God.

1. *Name three times in your life when you felt you were most inauthentic. Detail how your actions were different from how they should have been.*

(Since our teen years are normally marked with a search for identity, they are filled with experimentation in trying to find who we are. Include only one example from this time of your life.)

2. *How have you changed since those instances? What would you have done or how would you have acted differently now? If you have not changed, why not?*

3. *What is your biggest challenge to being authentic now?*

Perhaps you are held in high regard because of your position. Maybe God has given you an exceptional talent.

4. *What specific steps can you take to remain authentic?*

Given the challenge of remaining humble, what

can you do to remind yourself that it is not you but the Christ within who does the work?

5. The disciples argued over who was the greatest among them. When they asked Jesus, He said, "He who is least among you all is the one who is great" (Lk. 9:48). *Explain this seeming contradiction and how you can apply this teaching directly to your life.*

OFF THE MAIN TRAIL

One of the most famous of the Beatitudes is: "Blessed are the meek, for they shall inherit the earth" (Mt. 5:5). *What does this mean to you? What's the significance of the word* inherit?

STEPPING-STONE

Observe yourself.

Observe yourself. On a regular basis this week, detach yourself from what you are doing or how you are acting and just observe what is going on. This is especially important when you are interacting with others. Let a part of your brain that is not directly involved with what's going on observe exactly what you are doing. what you are saying, how you are acting, how you are reacting. Take a look at just what is going on. Are you acting happy? Are you reacting angrily? Are you worried?

Don't be judgmental. Just let part of you be a nonjudgmental nonparticipant in your life and take a good look at yourself.

It is not you but the Christ within which does the work.

SERVING GOD

If God lived on earth, people would break His windows.

—Jewish Proverb

Abraham Lincoln was introduced to a minister during the darkest days of the Civil War. The preacher told Lincoln that he and his entire congregation would be praying for him and the country. "Let us pray," intoned the minister, "that the Lord is on our side in this great struggle."

The President thanked the preacher for his kind thoughts and said, "I am not worried at all about that because I know that the Lord is always on the side of right; but it is my constant prayer that I and this nation may be on the Lord's side."

Lincoln knew what many of us forget from time to time: that God does not take sides. It is we who must take God's side. God will not change for us. We serve God. Our prayers, therefore, should be to stay centered in God's will, to serve God, and not to somehow try to manipulate God's will to serve us.

SOUL-TALK

I serve God.

1. _____

2. _____

3. _____

SOUL-THOUGHTS

CONSTANT CARE

Serving God takes constant watchfulness. As we repeat the habits of living, we too often act automatically, not stopping to think of exactly what we are doing and what we are saying with our actions. Our responses to circumstances, to our families, to our friends, to strangers, are too often automatic, based on how we have reacted in the past.

We, on *The Quest*, have been absorbing many life-transforming ideas as we have journeyed the path. Changes have been made in our thinking, no doubt. We could not have gotten to this point if that were not so. Yet have they been translated into daily action? We must continually search our souls.

1. *In what ways are you serving God in the major areas of your life? Write a sentence or two for each of the areas listed (and any other areas you can think of).*

Career:

Marriage or personal relationship:

Family:

Friends:

Neighbors:

Personal life:

Spiritual life:

2. *How can you serve God better in your day-to-day activities such as shopping, driving, talking to others, listening to others, and so on?*

3. *What are the most negative areas in your life?* Example: A troublesome co-worker.

What specific steps can you take to minimize your involvement with these areas?

4. *What are the most positive areas in your life? What specific steps can you take to increase your involvement with them?*

OFF THE MAIN TRAIL

"To simply know the truth is not enough ... the truth must ultimately be served."

What does this mean to you?

STEPPING-STONE

Write a complimentary note to a different person each day this week. Write to people who do not expect to hear from you.

You will feel wonderful sending these notes, and the people will feel wonderful receiving them. You'll have the satisfaction of having done a good thing, the people will feel pleased and blessed, and the world will be a little bit happier this week because of it.

You serve God.

TRUSTING GOD

*Woe to the man whose heart has not
learned while young to hope, to love—and
to put its trust in life.*

— Joseph Conrad

We had already climbed three hundred steps and were still not even halfway to the top! Legs aching, lungs begging for more air, we spiraled upward on the granite steps of the pointed steeple separated from a fall only by the skill of the stonemason's lacelike designs. We could easily see through the generous openings in the Gothic patterns as we wound our way upward. Yet it was difficult to believe that getting to the top of the world's tallest steeple would be worth the effort. But we trusted our friend who assured us that the view from atop the Ulm Cathedral was spectacular. He was right. After seven hundred sixty-eight steps we finally arrived at the top. It was indeed spectacular. The clear, crisp day yielded a view for miles of the Swabian Jura, the Alps, and the beautiful Danube River winding its way through the city. The day, the climb, and the fantastic view still linger in our minds today.

While frightening to us as we did it, the scary climb through the open stonework was a good part of the fun. Also, the physical exertion needed to make the climb would give us "bragging rights" whenever we told the story! We had trusted our friend who told us to go ahead and do it, and we were rewarded with a fun time, a sensational view, and wonderful memories.

All that because, in the midst of our physical discomfort and emotional fright, we decided to continue trusting our friend.

Imagine how much more is our reward when we trust God.

SOUL-TALK

 I trust God.

1. _____

2. _____

3. _____

SOUL-THOUGHTS

TRUST CAN'T BE TAUGHT

Trust is not something that can be taught. Trust comes from the level of feeling. Trusting God is really part of having faith in God, and faith is not an intellectual process—rather it comes directly from our hearts.

Trusting God is looking from the top of the mountain when you may be still in the valley. Trusting God is knowing that what you are presently going through is merely a stepping-stone to your higher good. That's not always easy. In fact, it seldom is.

The only activity in this Adventure, therefore, is a *Meditation in Trust* to enable you to allow trust to flood your life.

Meditation in Trust

(You may want to record this and play it back for yourself every day this week. Or you may choose to read it every day immediately before your regular meditation. Either way, let the words flow very, very slowly.)

I relax my mind and body now, and I turn my

attention away from the outer world toward that safe haven of peace within me. All is still ... all is still.

I connect with the Source of life ... I connect with God.

As I relax more deeply, I sense the great order of the universe ... season turning into season ... tides rising and falling ... planets traveling in their orbits ... constellations fixed in patterned beauty in the darkened sky.

Oh, the wonder of it all ... the miracle ... the love expressed in such creation.

For God so loved the world that it was destined to be good.

And I, as part of creation, am loved by that same Creator ... guided ... nurtured ... protected ... healed ... prospered. God knows my needs before I even ask, and so I simply trust, knowing that all is well.

I feel the presence and the power of God ... right now ... supporting me, loving me ... as I sit and I listen ... in the silence.

(Pause—allow the silence to surround you. When you feel so guided, you may continue.)

O God ... Great Spirit of this universe ... when I consider lilies of the field and small birds taking flight, I see Your gentle love and realize I am Your child, made in Your image and upheld by Your strength.

I release all human cares, resting easily, because I know that I am Yours ... always. My heart is overflowing with the joy of trusting You, God. All things in my life now have a sense of rightness to them ... and I am at peace.

STEPPING-STONE

Make a conscious effort to learn something new about a different person every day.

Learn what their favorite foods are or their favorite movies or where they went to school or what they like to read. Ask about their happiest memories of childhood. Let these people know that you are interested in them; be sincerely interested in what they say. It's difficult to learn anything about anyone else when you are talking, so be fully there in that place and that time.

You trust God.

One joy scatters a hundred griefs.
　　　　　—Chinese Proverb

We can wait for joy to be triggered by winning the lottery or by having someone express love for us or by our favorite team winning a game or by getting a hole in one. Still, if we wait for something to turn joy on, then something else will be able to turn joy off.

Joy is already ours. It is a gift from God instilled in us at our creation. Like love, it is always a part of us, always ready to be activated. We don't have to wait for something to throw our joy switch. We can activate it in ourselves, not because of what's going on in our lives, or even *in spite of* what's going on, but simply because *we are.*

God continually sends us joys. They come to us like birds seeking a nest, but if we do not acknowledge them, they sit and sing awhile in our soul, and then fly away.

I am filled with joy.

1. _____

2. _____

3. _____

SOUL-THOUGHTS

JOY IS EVERYWHERE

There is no circumstance that can force you to relinquish your joy. While it may seem absurd to think that it's possible to experience joy when a tragedy

strikes our lives, the fact remains that the *potential* for
joy exists at *every* moment. It is always we who decide
if it will express. It is always our decision. Yet our joy
can never be greater than the idea we have of it, simply
because joy is always an inside job.

1. *What physical act brings you the most joy?
Why?*

There are probably many physical things you do
that bring you joy: eating, sex, dancing, a hobby, and
many more. Choose one and write a few paragraphs
on why it makes you happy.

2. *What emotional thought or feeling brings you
the most joy? Why?*

This could include the feelings you get when you
are with a special person in your life or the feeling of
satisfaction with a job well done.

3. *What spiritual sensation brings you the most
joy? Why?*

   Perhaps you had a spiritual insight in your meditation that brought you great joy.

   4. *Compare the joy you feel in each of these areas.
Which is the most special, and how can you make that
joy more dominant in your life?*

5. *True* joy, since it comes from within, is always waiting to be experienced. It transcends any of the joys you listed in Activities 1 and 2.

Sit quietly, now, in a comfortable seat. As you relax your body and mind, think of the word joy as you inhale and exhale each breath. Then remain in the silence for several minutes as you allow the feelings of joy to bubble up from deep within you, sweeping through every cell of your body. Stay as long as you like in this state. When you are ready, slowly come back to the present reality, bringing the buoyancy of joy with you.

OFF THE MAIN TRAIL

Make note this week of all the things that bring you joy.

Joy comes not from circumstances themselves but from our adjustment to those circumstances. Be aware of the circumstances activating your joy. Was it reactive—was your joy dependent on changing circumstances? Or was your joy proactive—did you initiate the action yourself?

Keep score. Which joy was more dominant? Share the results with your friends if you are in a *Quest* group. Otherwise, write a page analyzing the results.

348

STEPPING-STONE

Strive to make someone happy.

It doesn't really matter what you do or to whom you do it, only that you try to make someone happy. Don't be limited to those you know or those you love. You can strive to make a stranger happy by letting him or her ahead of you in the supermarket or by allowing a car the right-of-way. You can give a compliment to your waiter or waitress. You can ask a co-worker if he or she needs help with a particular problem. You can show more interest in an acquaintance. Use your imagination. If you are serious about striving to make others happy this week, you will be shown the way.

You are filled with joy.

*If a man does not keep pace with his companions,
perhaps it is because he hears a different
drummer. Let him step to the music which he
hears, however measured or far away.*
                    —Henry David Thoreau

Where and when does your path begin? It begins exactly where you are at precisely the moment you decide you want to experience the presence of God in your life. That place is where you are right now and that time is as you read these words because the decision to experience the presence of God is made and remade at each moment.

SOUL-TALK

 I want to know You more.

1. _____

2. _____

3. _____

WHERE ARE YOU LOOKING?

Like the high-wire walker, you can't stay where you are. Remember, the performer didn't look at his feet, because that only told him where he was. We can't look at where we are either. We have to keep focused on the path to know we are going in the right direction.

1. *As clearly as you can, identify the path you are on right now.*

This may be challenging because the path is seldom a clearly defined course but rather a nebulous journey that we often sense more than see.

2. *List the times in your life that you took a serious detour from the path.*

There are some obvious situations that shout to be noticed, like a drug addiction or a criminal life. However, don't forget the more subtle detours (such as destructive relationships) that may have taken you off the path for extended periods, or a blind ambition to succeed that may have deflected you from the path.

3. *What got you back on the path?* How was it that you decided to get back on the path?

4. *What keeps you on the path now?* Why are

you staying on the path again?

5. *What is the most serious deterrent to your staying on the path now?* Is there a personal relationship or a set of circumstances or an emotional attachment to something that keeps you from seeking more of the knowledge of the presence of God in your life?

In what specific ways can you address this dilemma? What lessons that you have learned from the past can help you with this?

OFF THE MAIN TRAIL

Write a short autobiography in which you describe the main crossroads in your life from the time you remember making your first important decision to the present. Show the continuum of how each major step related to the next to bring you to where you are today.

STEPPING-STONE

Write the following statements in large letters on a number of index cards and post them in very prominent places where you will see them throughout the day.

Repeat them silently or aloud as often as possible each day this week.

"I now release everyone and everything that is not part of my divine path."

"I now attract everyone and everything that is part of my divine path."

You may want to say your "release" statement as often as possible before noon and your "attract" statement from noon on. But no matter how you use these statements, they are a powerful combination.

You want to know God more.

*Y*OUR UNIQUE WAY

You have sought His face, and you must begin to
express something of His nature.

—Emmet Fox

The streets are filled with ghosts and goblins, witches and ghouls. Men are dressed as women and women dressed as men. Bears and bunnies knock on doors asking for treats while walking skeletons fill the night. The most outlandish creatures appear.

Halloween is a fun time because it gives us all a chance to dress up as something we're not. Costumes are a gross distortion of our uniqueness. That's the fun of costumes.

Yet what about the subtle disguises we use to deviate from who and what we are? What about the anger we are capable of showing? Is that part of our core, part of God? What about the fear or worry we display? What about an unforgiveness we hold on to? Are these really expressions of God or are they costumes, disguises we wear, detours on the path?

You would not be this far along *The Quest* if you did not feel a calling to walk the path. There is a unique trail for you and you alone. Some can walk with you part of the way but, from time to time, you must leave them and go it alone.

SOUL-TALK

I have a special gift.

1. _____

2. _____

3. _____

SOUL-THOUGHTS

ONE OF A KIND

It is said that there are no two snowflakes alike. Each of these six-pointed clusters of ice crystals is made up of beautifully branched columns, needles, and irregular forms. Each is a unique expression of the water vapor and freezing temperature that created it. If each tiny snowflake is completely different, completely unique, just imagine how uniquely different we are, not only physically, but in our emotions, opinions, reactions, likes, dislikes, and sensibilities.

1. You are a unique expression of that which made you—God. You are unique not only physically, but emotionally and spiritually.

List your areas of uniqueness and how you differ from most people you know. This would include your likes and dislikes, your emotional reactions to certain circumstances, your spiritual feelings. Be as inclusive in each area as you can.

Physically:

Emotionally:

Spiritually:

   2. *Are you celebrating your uniqueness in these areas, or do you attempt to hide it so that you will blend in with those around you? Analyze why you act as you do.*

It is tempting to follow others' paths with them, especially the path of someone whom you love and respect. A friend may tell you of her spiritual teacher. You are regaled with stories of what this guru did for your friend, how her life has changed, how she will never be the same. In deference to your friend, you may try to adapt your unique way into your friend's way, but it can't be done. If you surrender your uniqueness to try to clone someone else's, you will fail miserably at being yourself.

God did not create you to be someone else. God created someone else to be someone else! You were created to be you. The degree to which you get in touch with that special expression of God—the Christ of you—is the degree to which your life will be peace-filled and the degree to which you will experience the authentic joy of being one with God.

In a certain Native American religion, it is taught that when we are conceived, the gods give us a gift. The gift could be the gift of teacher or healer or that of peacemaker or builder or an infinite number of other gifts. They teach that to the extent that we use our unique gift and share it with others, we are happy. Conversely, to the extent that we withhold our unique gift, we are unhappy.

3. *Do you feel you were given a unique gift to share? If so, what is that gift?* What does that still, small voice within you say you should be doing with your life? *Are you using your gift? If so, how are you using it? If not, why not, and how can you begin using it?*

Staying on *The Quest* has needed a strong commitment, as you know. In coming this far you have committed time and resources to changing your life. Hopefully your unique way of expressing God has been made clearer to you, and you are beginning to be more and more authentic as that uniqueness expresses.

OFF THE MAIN TRAIL

We depend on each other, that is part of our nature. Depending on someone, however, is not the same as finding our identity in that person. This is particularly true in relationships. If we are to belong to a group or have a relationship with a person, it should be out of strength. If we seek another's strength to fulfill our perceived weakness, or if another seeks us to fulfill his or her weakness, then it's a poor relationship, one which will stunt emotional and spiritual growth. If someone says, "I can't live without you," it's time to reconsider the relationship, because we can never live happily with a person who can't live without us. The object of a relationship is not to share weaknesses but rather to share strengths. We choose someone who can enjoy our unique personality because this person has identified a unique personality of his or her own.

List the important relationships in your life. (You will want to use your separate journal for this.)

Answer the following questions for each relationship:

1. Are you in the relationship because you are trying to strengthen a perceived weakness of your own?

2. Are you able to be uniquely yourself?

3. Does the other person enjoy your being uniquely yourself?

4. Are you able to enjoy the other person for being his or her unique self?

STEPPING-STONE

Let love be your guide.

Allow *every* decision you make this week—*every* decision—to be motivated by love. If there is a conflict between your heart and your head, follow your heart. This may take some getting used to because so many decisions are made automatically. This week, slow down. Allow your heart to get involved.

You have a special gift.

Even beyond what we ask, seek, earn, or deserve under the law, God is more than willing to give.

—Charles Fillmore

According to the law of mind action, thoughts held in mind produce after their kind. Yet not every thought you have thought has resulted in a corresponding effect. For example, how many times have you thought you had a malady—perhaps dwelled on it for days, convinced that your body had developed a certain disease—only to find out that you were fine? Those negative thoughts did not translate into sickness. Why? Because grace acts as a buffer between harmful thoughts and their corresponding effects.

SOUL-TALK

I live in God's grace.

1. _____

2. _____

3. _____

_____

SOUL-THOUGHTS

_____

GRACE WORKS BOTH WAYS

Whereas God's grace acts as a spiritual shock absorber to lessen the immediate negative effects of our negative thoughts, grace also acts as a catalyst to our positive, God-centered thoughts. Rather than slowing down the effects of these positive thoughts, it speeds them up. Why? For the same reason that you can get a boat going faster rowing *with* the current than rowing against it.

You have read again and again in *The Quest* that God's will for us is absolute good. God's good is a mighty river in which we are immersed that invites us to flow with it toward all good things. While we are always part of that river, we choose how we want to proceed in it.

The river is God's grace, and we can float peacefully in it and be taken gently and steadily toward our good. Or we can seek to go faster in this steady flow by working with God and our spiritual selves. Or we can fight the flow. We can anchor ourselves in the middle of the river, refusing to move. But the flow will constantly tug at us, urging us in the direction of our good.

God's grace is a gently and steadily flowing river of love that *always* coaxes us toward the wonder that God has for us. We can fight it, we can flow with it, we can work with it, but we can't ignore it. It is part of us, and we are part of it. As we said, it may be God's most unique gift to us.

Thank You, God, for Your grace.

1. *List the times in your life when you feel God's grace saved you from a "deserved" fate.*

2. *Picture yourself in a safe vessel floating in a gently flowing stream. You know the current is heading toward your good, that sublime peace and great joy await you. Would you just drift or would you row?*

What about your life? You are immersed in a gently flowing current of God's love. Do you feel you are moving in the direction of the flow?

If so, are you drifting or actively rowing the boat?

If not, what can you do to "get in the flow"?

3. *Select one of the following images for a meditation:*

a. You are in a wide, sunny meadow. The air is warm with a sky that's almost golden with the brilliance of the sun. The grass is vivid green and dotted with a festival of wildflowers—white, pink, yellow, red, and lavender blue. The atmosphere is sweet with their perfume. Weaving round your head are yellow butterflies, their iridescent wings shining as they float on the gentle breeze. The songs of birds drift across the broad lea, sharing their joy with anyone who happens by.

b. You are at the edge of the sea. The air is warm and moist and bears a saltiness which settles on your lips. The packed sand is firm, unmoving as small waves splash gently around your feet. The foamy spindrift from the rolling waves blows playfully off the water and scampers up the beach like large, fluffy cotton balls. Overhead are gulls, dipping their wings at the blue sea and calling to each other.

After you mentally place yourself in one of these scenes, begin to feel weightless, as if gravity were no longer strongly holding you to the Earth. See yourself skipping freely—in slow motion—through the imaginary scene. Your arms and legs move in a dance of sheer joy, as an unseen Power lifts and carries you from step to step.

Each time you do this meditation increase your sense of total freedom and effortlessness.

OFF THE MAIN TRAIL

What about the "other" son in the Prodigal Son story? What are your feelings about how he was treated? How does the concept of grace apply to him? Do you identify with this son or with the "prodigal"? Why?

STEPPING-STONE

Affirm your worth.

Every morning upon awakening and every evening before you go to bed, look at yourself in the mirror and affirm your worth. Tell yourself out loud that you are worthwhile. Give yourself a terrific compliment. Remind yourself that God actually loves you and thinks you are important to the universe.

You live in God's grace.

There is more to life than increasing its speed.

—Mahatma Gandhi

"The Simple Life" is a life of unadorned humility. It is a life of unpretentious authenticity. It is a life that is anchored at the divine nucleus of who and what we are: highly cherished and very intimate expressions of the great Creative Force that made us. It is a life that is lived as a constant expression of why we were created: to know God, to love God, and to serve God. There is nothing more elementary than that; there is nothing more important than that.

Of course, *simple* is not always *easy*, and the simple life is not necessarily an easy one to live in our fast-paced, "instant-gratification" world. To know, to love, and to serve God is a full-time commitment, one which never leaves our awareness. In fact, unless it is the one principle on which all thoughts, deeds, and actions are founded, there is no simple life because, without God at its center, life takes on complexities.

SOUL-TALK

God is enough.

1. _____

2. _____

3. _____

SOUL-THOUGHTS

THE QUEST CONTINUES

The completion of this book does not signal the completion of your quest. You know that. *The Quest* is a never-ending search to express the divinity in you that is eager to be free, hungry to embrace again its Creator. This past year of being on *The Quest* has given you impetus to continue that search. A retrospective of this past year will help you to see where you began, how you proceeded, and where you are now.

1. *Taking your time, this week review your answers, notes, and comments in this Activity Book. Especially reread your* Soul-Thoughts, *which should be like a journey of your quest.*

2. *What is the single most significant thing you learned while on* The Quest?

3. *What do you consider to be your greatest triumph this past year? What aspect of your transformation has been the most important?*

4. *What do you feel must still be accomplished by you? What specific plans do you have for achieving this?*

5. Write a short summation of your feelings at having finished this year of growth and try to comprehend how far you have come since you first heard the call to begin The Quest.

6. The end of every quest has a prize. What is the prize which you attained? What will you do with it?

7. We have reached the end of our journey together. Where do you go from here?

STEPPING-STONE

 Choose your favorite Stepping-Stone *and practice
it.*

In your review of this Activity Book, select one
Stepping-Stone, one that you found most meaningful.
Incorporate it (or them) into your life for this week ... or
this month ... or this year ... or this lifetime.

God is enough.

Now please return to the Guidebook so that we can share a few brief,
final moments together.

Printed in the U.S.A.

152-11216-5C-8-05 Q